QUERENCIA SUMMER 2022

QUERENCIA

Querencia Press, LLC
Chicago Illinois

OTHER TITLES FROM QUERENCIA

Allison by Marisa Silva-Dunbar

GIRL. by Robin Williams

Retail Park by Samuel Millar

Every Poem a Potion, Every Song a Spell by Stephanie Parent

QUERENCIA PRESS

© Copyright 2022

LIBRARY OF CONGRESS CATALOG-IN-PUBLICATION DATA

ISBN 979 8 98607 886 1

.

www.querenciapress.com

First Published in 2022

Querencia Press, LLC
Chicago IL

Printed & Bound in the United States of America

Poetry 11

are we – Sarah Corwin 12

I Freeze, everytime – Emily Eerie 13

Yellow – Emily Eerie 14

Dorothy – Emily Eerie 15

Settling In – Christina Hennemann 16

Canticle – Kate MacAlister 18

Guerilla Girl Art – Kate MacAlister 20

Eat the Rich – Kate MacAlister 21

dearself – Alexis Hernandez.................................... 23

you (I wish) – Alexis Hernandez 24

Daughter of Venus – Jillian Calahan....................... 25

Funny How – Jillian Calahan.................................... 27

Whosthe Cosmonaut – Lev Verlaine....................... 28

Keep Close. – Lev Verlaine 29

Mars 2002. – Lev Verlaine....................................... 30

Odyssey of the Hine's Emerald Dragonfly – Daniel Moreschi...... 31

Invasion – Faye Alexandra Rose.............................. 33

The Mourning Cycle – Faye Alexandra Rose 34

To Be a Woman (T/W: Infertility) – Faye Alexandra Rose 38

The Ballad of Maddy and Cassie – Marisa Silva-Dunbar............. 39

Bluebeard's Harem – Marisa Silva-Dunbar.............. 41

Vorfreude – Marisa Silva-Dunbar............................ 42

Rapunzel – Emma Wells... 43

Cake and Jelly Cream – Mimi Flood 45

Pretty Words – Mimi Flood...................................... 46

A Knife in between my Thighs – Mimi Flood 47

Inch by second – Sana Mujtaba 48

Satellite heart – Sana Mujtaba 49

Sacrosanct – Emily Perkovich 50

Red and Blue (TW) – Alice Carroll...51

Shared Sickness (TW) – Alice Carroll 52

Firth of Morning – Tom Squitieri 54

The Weeping Woman – Tom Squitieri 55

Crooked Rockpools – Tiggy Chadwick 58

Life Isn't Enough When You Have Time – adam Shove 61

Faucet Salt – adam Shove..63

A love letter to my younger self – Lilith Kerr...............................65

Rage // Nurture – Lilith Kerr 66

I can't go back to Pittsburgh – Amanda Brown 68

After 20 Hours of Labor, My Baby is Ready to Be Born, But We
have to Wait – Amanda Brown 69

Untitled – Courtney Written...70

Inheritance – Jordan Nishkian 71

The story of two breakdowns – Jordan Nishkian 73

The common heritage of all our awkward bodies//Of mice,
machines, and miracles//Thank you for making me feel welcome
in the world – Sascha Felix Luinenburg 76

Cinder Girl Grows Wings – Stephanie Parent...............................78

Blessed Curse – Stephanie Parent..80

Watch Hill Park – Rhys Campbell..82

This Heart Holds Only Grief (a series of drafts) – Robin Williams 83

I TOOK MY CAT TO THE VET AND THE WORLD REMINDS ME OF EVERYTHING I'M MISSING – Robin Williams 85

RUST – Basil 86

Daughter of Bones – Emily Perina 94

Untitled – Emily Perina 95

Addicted – Sara Sabharwal 96

Secrets & Sins – Sara Sabharwal 97

Forgiveness has Eight Wobbly Legs – Tyler Hurula 98

So Mad He Can't See Straight – Tyler Hurula 100

To the Man on the Dating App Who Doesn't Understand Why I didn't Reply Because I'm Fat and Polyamorous – Tyler Hurula . 103

Ramshackle Skeleton – Asher Phoenix 105

Dark Halo – Asher Phoenix 107

Grandfather – Joe Espinoza 109

Comfort – Pop 110

The old house – Pop 111

Sometimes all you want is to be saved – Ishita Ganguly 112

To a Conflicted Catholic Lesbian, From a Trans Girl – Mia-Jo Feeley 113

The cis girl wants to know what your body looks like and doesn't mind the blood on her hands – Mia-Jo Feeley 117

The TSA Took My Penis Away – Mia-Jo Feeley 118

the book of aberration – Lindsay Valentin 119

the wanton want – Lindsay Valentin 120

Waves – Christina D. Rodriguez 122

Phases of Being a Daughter – Christina D. Rodriguez 125

Mad Gowns – Christina D. Rodriguez 130

Hiding From You at the Hopyard Alehouse – Abbey Lynne Rays 133

Still I Hope – Abbey Lynne Rays.................................135

The body as a talisman – Kristiana Reed 136

I like melancholy, so I write in the past tense – Nabila Abid......137

Hijab – Nabila Abid 138

Cherried Knees – Rachel Jacobs/Phantasma...............139

The Temple of Athena – Rachel Jacobs/Phantasma 140

BETWEEN THE RIPTIDES – T.C. Anderson..................142

RESUSCITATE – T.C. Anderson 143

IF IT HAD BEEN ANOTHER ME AND ANOTHER SUMMER – T.C. Anderson 145

PMT – Claire Thom 146

Life Lesson – Claire Thom 147

Static – Claire Thom..149

Synthetic Worship – Jessica Berry 150

I spend the afternoon imagining our marriage – Jessica Berry..151

Bookology – Jessica Berry..152

I want Janet Weiss on drums – Carlos Clark...............154

ALZHEIMERS – Omobola Osamor................................155

SEX – Omobola Osamor...157

CROOKED – Kait Quinn 158

JESUS CHRIST, I'M SO BLUE ALL THE TIME *After Phoebe Bridgers* – Kait Quinn...159

The Neon Girls – Fiona Dignan 160

I Dream of Foxes – Fiona Dignan 161

And how many children do you have? – Fiona Dignan.............. 163

Counterfeit Saint – Eddie Brophy.. 164

September's Lost – Eddie Brophy 165

Odd Uncovering – Georgina Melendez.. 166

Be Not Her Strength – Georgina Melendez 167

An OK State Motto – Amanda Karch... 168

Leaving Eden – Amanda Karch 169

She Was Asking For It – Amanda Karch 170

Tale of the Unseen – Liz Yew 171

IMAGINING ADVICE FROM MY OLD PSYCHIATRIST – Daniel J. Flore
III 172

HALLUCINATING WHILE MY FRIEND SMOKES POT AND LOOKS AT
ME LIKE I'M JESUS – Daniel J. Flore III.. 173

We – Michael Brigden.. 174

Cause and Effect – Michael Brigden 175

THE ODE TO "O" – Effie Spence 176

a stretch to me – Effie Spence 178

THREE SISTERS – Effie Spence 179

Mirror Image – Ryan Kenny 180

The Garden, After Rachel Long – Rebecca Green 181

Reflections – Rebecca Green 183

Cake – Rebecca Green 184

Nothing, Killing *After Emily Skaja* – Shilo Niziolek 185

So You Wanna Talk About How I'm The Dead Girl In The Painting
– Shilo Niziolek 189

We All Got Burnt *After Olivia Gatwood* – Shilo Niziolek............ 192

Women – Bharti Bansal 197

Language – Bharti Bansal 200

Fiction 204

Mr. Cameron – Amelia Jacob......................................205

The Lady and the Octopus. – Alice Whiting.................212

What Will It Take – Asher Phoenix 215

Jane gets a promotion – Kristiana Reed 220

A Married Woman's Story: a response to Katherine Mansfield's 'A Married Man's Story'. – Kristiana Reed......................225

What Do You See When You Close Your Eyes? – Madeleine S. Cargile 228

"Do You Like Me Now?" – Madeleine S. Cargile 232

Animal – PD Hogan 235

Teeth – PD Hogan 237

THE MAGE'S APPRENTICE – Estelle Grace Tudor 239

Bathwater – Jordan Nishkian......................................243

Broken Record – Gabrielle Pelayo 247

Non-Fiction 252

Heaven Has a Broken Door – Brendaliz Torres...........253

Keep Families Together – Savannah Verdin 257

About the Contributors 262

POETRY

are we – Sarah Corwin (she/her)

you'd come by

and we'd zip ourselves together

and I'd try very hard to know it was happening

because it seemed like something I'd want to know about

I'd try very hard

and eventually,

yes

I knew

and I didn't have to try anymore

so I turned to you,

and said

See?

See how we're here?

and you said….

and you said….

what *did* you say exactly…

I Freeze, everytime – Emily Eerie (she/her)

I feel a magnet behind my sternum, pulling my chest way deep down. A concave scrying bowl to match my frown. If I don't react, give you the satisfaction, am I complicit in my own public humiliation? If I react...I mark myself the victim, they'll chorus "it really wasn't as she says". Sometimes I wonder if my voice would be louder if I were dead. They'd tut their tongues, look at the martyr in repose, Didn't the poor dear know, What happens when you don't wear more clothes? I should just stay silent or risk the rage in my boy's eyes, walk out the front door, as he shoves a man into the bar side. I should have just said something, the first hand on my arm. Didn't want to make a fuss, benefit of the doubt, there's no harm. I should have just stayed home, safe as houses, right? What's a girl to do in the harsh nightlife? I should have punched his teeth in, when he grabbed my ass. I should have just done something beyond shattering like glass. I guess I'm the fucking victim, done that dance before. Every time I think that I've healed completely, I come on back for more, I come on back for more. I feel dirty, attention seeking. I'll fight for any person but for myself when I'm weeping. No one gives a shit how I handle this, mostly because no one will ever really forgive. Oh, forgive me. Babe, forgive me. God, forgive me. Someone forgive me.

Yellow – Emily Eerie (she/her)

Rot the wood box that holds your heart, I'll be strong. I won't fall apart. Break your bones to make my bread, I won't cry. I'll be stone instead. And, when the last piece of you within me dies, I'll laugh, I'll sing, to the heavens to the skies. And, when you've had your final say, I'll dance, I'll dance, in yellow on your grave. I'll dance, I'll dance, in yellow on your grave. Sometimes we're the only person we can save. I'll dance, I'll dance, in yellow on your grave. Sometimes we're the only person we can save.

Dorothy – Emily Eerie (she/her)

We have a pack of whispers, a coven full of sisters. Thrown over by the misters, blood in our whiskers. We're angry and we're stewing, the sort of poison that's been brewing, since the time of Cain and Abel, since before radio and cable. Since rocks and sticks and bricks, since switches and kisses and misses, since time itself woke up one morning to greet the sun, since the first time a girl learned to run. How is it every woman I know has that secret history etched upon her soul? How is it every woman I know has a word, a sentence, a chapter or a trilogy that comes out slowly with coaxing and empathy? How is it so many women have been afraid, and so many men are certain they've never met a monster in their life? I wonder sometimes if I'm culpable, responsible, for the impact of your hurricane, for the water stains, for the clogged-up drains, the damage done to property, to mind, to minds, to bodies. I was an island, I felt your wrath, long before you reached any distant shores. I bunkered down and ignored the sounds of trees falling, far, and far away from me. Maybe, I'm not the only girl frozen in your hurricane, swirling in your cyclone. Maybe, I'm not the only woman who freezes even now, at the briefest thought of you. A child's hands were pressed against your chest, your hurricane broke everything, until there was nothing but the pieces of me left. I have nightmares of wind whipping, faces I don't yet know. I wish I could be a good little witch, and ensure the other Dorothies get home. Oh, there's somewhere over the rainbow, closure, so they say. But, I wonder if I'm allowed to lay amongst the poppies, on the bad days? Oh, there's no place like home, There's no place like home. There's no place like home, and I, and I, and I, and I, and I haven't been home in years. Haven't been home in years, haven't been home in years.

Settling In – Christina Hennemann (she/her)

The electric shower is whirring,
hot water reddens my sore skin.
It's near to impossible, a struggle
to find the perfect temperature.

I'm living my dream in my house by the sea.

The heaters are thrumming but still
it's cold, damp, noisily solitary.
The dusty heat evaporates so fast,
the old walls of my house can barely
keep it in, hold me close, hug me tight.

I wander to the draughty window,
glare at the gushing sea.
My eyes glaze at the sight of the turquoise waves.

I'm not used to the cold, the old, the electricity.
I set the timer: click and shower—
an appointment for cleaning my freezing limbs.
It is strange,

        or am I?

My neighbours have the heat turned off.

I walk the golden strand, glowing in sunbeams,
wrapped in a vibrant, salty breeze.
My ears listen to sea shell music.

With stiff, blue lips, I smile and frown,
fixated on the aquamarine horizon.

I am home—
yet,
it's different from home.

Canticle – Kate MacAlister (she/her)

all the battles
of every day
burn our candle
low

let me take you
deep
into the forest
where
light breeds in the dark

Would it be too much?
Would it be impolite?

to offer you my blood
flowers
in a porcelain bowl of moonlight
by the sleeping river

where we hungered
where we touched

Death became small
remained heavy
stars falling from your eyes
through my bones
burning my roughened edges

nothing can feed
the wilderness of mine
but the sound of your soft voice

I hear
the whispered song of
your scars in
the night

nothing can feed
the soft fauna of mine
but the sound of your wild heart

all my scratches and stitches
utter but one prayer

please don't change your mind

maybe
this is where
courage blossoms

Guerilla Girl Art – Kate MacAlister (she/her)

you tell me
you read this book
countless beautiful absurdities
a story cabinet filled to the brim
with poison and wine
something strange to behold
prehistoric as
bone fires
or the silence of men

*"He painted flowers on her starving body,
Blue orchids and Valerian in the dying night"*

so I pick up my pen to
trace your
tiger stripes
and ley lines
back home
by the light
of stars
blossoming
beneath your eyes

Eat the Rich – Kate MacAlister (she/her)

thighs slapping
rippled and torn
butterfly skin
brings the thunder
starts a red-hot fire
creates a storm
in the silent
time of monsters
and blood

calories or ribs counted
it doesn't really matter
it's all only a cage for the
same
voracious
ferocious
vicious
Beast
they named

the bitch
that slut
this woman

so afraid
so desperate to keep us
tame
so worried

if
we
just
eat

we will devour this world

dearself – Alexis Hernandez (she/her)

Youlayinthewastelandwithfears
eversoclosetobecomingone
Yourunrampantinyourmindasyourwordstwistandlie
AsIremainaprisonertoyou,
mymind
mychains
Yourconsequenceisthistoilinmydreamsthatawakenthe
darkestpartsofme
BegoneIsaytoyou
Thisvibrantmonsterthatensues
Feedingmeindolence
Causingmetofeeldumbnoless
Imustlearntoloveyounow
Youaremeandyouaremycrown
Agildedcrownaqueentomy
EagerforthetearsIcry
Thesweetflowwillteachme
Howto*grow*

you (I wish) – Alexis Hernandez (she/her)

How can I aspire to be anything other than?
The vibrant petals of their serene beauty
Outshines that of my uniquity
Skinny and tall I fall
To the pits of my despair as I conquer
The fear of being overlooked
Overthrown
This princess should know
That she cannot be overruled by girls in tight clothes
However strong my mind is
I follow behind
For my mind is wishing that I was
You

Daughter of Venus – Jillian Calahan (she/her/they)

My mother said the Earth
trembled in her belly
as I was born.
Boulders crumbled at her hips.
Soil turned with every push
until I arrived on a mudslide
of blood, sweat, and tears.
16 days late because
I'm just that stubborn.
I was forced from her womb
with a Pitocin packed punch
and I've been angry ever since.
Hotheaded,
I came into this world screaming.
With hair the color of flames
and the beginnings of horns
that would grow in later
when I learned of monsters.
Real monsters.
Human monsters.

I was taught to grind my horns down
until they were no longer visible,
because little girls are soft.
Little girls don't yell.
Little girls don't argue.
Little girls don't talk back.
Good little girls listen.

Good little girls stay quiet.
Good little girls obey.
But I'm not a little girl anymore.
I will no longer speak so softly
that my words float away.
I will no longer have my passion
be mistaken for selfishness.
I will plant myself
among the thorns and weeds
and I will rise like the bull
I was born to be.
I will make Venus proud.

Funny How – Jillian Calahan (she/her/they)

Funny how they ask us what
we were wearing
when it happened.
As if short skirts have *Fuck Me*
stitched right into the fabric.
Yet you never hear of a man
assaulting a mannequin
in a little black dress.
Funny how it was never about the clothes.

Funny how we are told
that we are too sensitive
when masculinity is so fragile
it shatters from a single **NO**.

Funny how you think of us as weak
when we are forced to carry the weight of
societal expectations,
the burden of motherhood,
beauty standards,
or our rapist's child.

Funny how a woman's place is in the kitchen
but you're the ones feeding us bullshit,
and we're no longer accepting it.

Funny how we're not laughing anymore.

Whosthe Cosmonaut – Lev Verlaine *(he/him)*

I'm the way I've made me—
                growing world rot,
          ripe from Eve's tree.
On palm-top graces, Love will do its dying crawl
upon fruit stained fingers, bled red.Upon me.

Of blood for blood,And the effort of holding it to the skin.
          I couldn't help but become one of
               my mother's dead.

        Itry to think of
the experiences I've had, and the life I've lived and I
  can't remember who it is she's been calling forth.

Maybe it's time I stopped believing
those around me are made up of ignorances,
that hate and love can coexist in a single form.

For when the heat turns over—
Despite all anger I remain the same.

Keep Close. – Lev Verlaine *(he/him)*

And
He's starved for sickness. A makeshift man//
pseudo sentient custom flesh.Will anybody
look at me?I'm not going to let someone fuck
what they want to see. My greatest fear is being
undesirable.

I sleep like a skyscraper´s suicide
victim, missing a place of hatred// Would we
know love if we didn't know it? There's so much to tell
about being alive// So let me.

 Surviving winter is the hardest part.
Bury me and they´ll defrost
 new womb.

Chapel boy from
a cracked knuckle. Does he know I've been hoping for
someone to notice me like I notice everyone else?
Boys can´t cry So I will.Can no one tell whatI´m
making myself to be. Art is the necessary evil.

Mars 2002. – Lev Verlaine *(he/him)*

I´ve been aching to go down half south,find God's field.
I want to meet a real cowboy. Make plans to fuck off with.

       I've gotta get curious.

Maybe I'll find it, get buried in it.They'll rip me right out the dirt
forced back in the flesh.
I don't want to be a man,I want to kill him
      butI know I'd be miserable standing over your dirt.

        You're out on Sunday street making it look holy
          they're saying your name and
          waiting for you to jump the phase.

Ask what comes from a sit down life, because this feeling
this is decay too.
Ripe enough to pluck the flowers from
my flesh swells and soon blooms.

I can't live here.I can't live.

        If not here, life elsewhere is still an option.

Odyssey of the Hine's Emerald Dragonfly – Daniel Moreschi
(he/him)

A mother roams nemoral bounds, where roots and rims encase
The malleable solace of a sunken ark's embrace
As dips and oscillations from a dragon's tail foretell
A latent dormancy within a leafy citadel.

A new-born is denied repose and famished pores collect
The layers of a shell as a falling cradle feigns neglect.
It braves a bed of swaddling swings, that brings an abyssal brink:
The nascence of a nymph amid the liquid lanes to slink.

Along a luminous roulette of planted palisades,
Where droves of small amalgams mass as aqua masquerades
And dainty strides belie the plunders of a vital script,
When carcasses are catalysts for stratums to be stripped.

From gulfs of gills and guillotines that guard the river banks,
To navigating chancy streams, while spurred by sprouting flanks.
A final shed at shallow depths, and then a brisk ascent
Of paper pillars on a pressing urge to reinvent.

On brace of motes, to break the mould, as quaking seams unearth,
A base of beats await the wands of wander from rebirth.
When coated peaks embolden leaps, a lustrous yarn combines,

And reaches to the heights to leave behind the leaves as Hine's.

Invasion – Faye Alexandra Rose (she/her)

My mother's body planted seeds

sprouting fists beneath the skin—

poison that lies dormant

until plucked from the soil.

> *A mutation, a mass, a bud,*
>
> *warns of its immersive hell.*

Sowing uncertainty, scattering

grateful *I love yous* and *hugs*—

the weed that arrogated her garden

will soon wilt and decompose.

> *Thawed and weathered,*
>
> *she lives to see summer.*

The Mourning Cycle – Faye Alexandra Rose (she/her)

My grandmother both entered and left the earth alone

for nobody escapes the reaper once he decides your end,

the people left alive are the ones left with the pain of
longing,

cursed with the burden of not forgetting and to never be
forgotten—

there is nothing quite like death that has you questioning life

—just some of the hardships that come with experiencing
loss.

I wipe tears from my mother's cheeks beside a coffin filled
with loss.

I comfort her, reminding her that she will not have to grieve
alone

as her children and their love will surround her throughout
her life,

and it is only the body that's buried, her mother's memories
do not end:

the photographs above the mantlepiece won't let her be
forgotten,

place our fingertips around the frame when we're deep in
longing.

As years pass by, we become less haunted by the ghost of longing,

its presence no longer fills the air when we sit with our loss.

Our minds now calmer and specific details have been forgotten,

like the sound of her voice no longer echoes when we're alone

and the scent of her perfume brings comfort and not remembrance of her end

as we hold on to our loved one's dearly, with a new appreciation for life.

Every year on the sixth day of June, we come together and celebrate her life.

She is no longer living, and our hearts are once more filled with longing—

consumed with nostalgia, photo albums in our laps, not wanting the evening to end.

For it's moments like these when you become engulfed by their absence, of loss,

when the chair sits empty, and her glasses are still perched on the shelf alone—

we are without her body, but the warmth of June is never forgotten.

But as the sun continues to orbit, the seasons forget and are forgotten

and you curse the day you wished for autumn to wash away summer's life,

when the chill steals the comfort and reminds you that you are alone

with no one to hold now that winter's grasp is firmly around your body, longing

for you to recall her warmth and reminisce on past days, of loss

now that the leaves fall, and the sun has come to a sudden end.

The feeling of grief feels unfamiliar as we now approach my mother's end.

When life lives on, the feeling of grief inevitably gets forgotten

and when another leaves the earth, we are overcome with loss

mourning the fragility and beauty of yet another's life.

As time slips through our fingertips, we're stuck with hopeless longing,

standing in a crowd of family and friends yet never feeling more alone.

Why does an ending have to feel like the end?

When the spirit departs us toward the other life.

Earth is not the final stop and that cannot be forgotten

when remembering feels heavy and you are deep in longing.

For everyone has or will experience loss

and that sentiment itself should make you feel less alone.

To Be a Woman (T/W: Infertility) – Faye Alexandra Rose
(she/her)

Am I less of a woman? My body has failed me,
a stork dropped empty shells at my door and flew,
fertility is a ghost that haunted me daily.

I never felt the urge to bounce a babe on my knee,
girls at school had lists; one pink and one blue,
am I less of a woman? My body has failed me.

During my adolescence I explored bodies freely,
yet my womb laid dormant, and worries grew,
fertility is a ghost that haunted me daily.

An ex-boyfriend left when I turned twenty
five, years of failed attempts, I gave in and withdrew,
fertility is a ghost that haunted me daily.

I now stare at single lines and fall to my knees
my instinct to become a mother is ripping me in two,
am I less of a woman? My body is failing me.

And the clock ticks faster having past thirty
doctors confirm what I thought to be true.
Am I less of a woman? My body is failing me,
fertility is a ghost, and it haunts me daily.

The Ballad of Maddy and Cassie – Marisa Silva-Dunbar
(she/her)

"[Cassie] fell in love with every guy she ever dated...she didn't like to be alone."
—Euphoria

Maddy is armor and metallic war paint, her hair holds an invisible crown. Cassie is posed innocent, all iridescent tears staining pink cheeks as she surrounds herself with garlands of blush-colored roses hoping a boy will notice her orgasmic writhing on a carousel horse. He will fall in love, steal into the night—rescue her from washing dishes, loneliness, her 4 a.m.

morning makeup routine. Maddy dreams of luxury, knows her wit and eyeliner must be a sharp guillotine, ready to demolish any hater or traitor. She is bedazzled, can play the damsel—but she knows she will be the one to claw her way out of destruction. Maddy and Cassie used to dance the night away:

hands linked in the dark as they shimmied and body rolled—glitter gleaming, their magic created sparks as everyone watched in awe. Cassie said she was Maddy's best friend, Maddy told her "bitch, you're my soulmate." Cassie cradled Maddy when Maddy's home life would start to quake—

promised the pain wouldn't last. On nights Cassie felt deflated, Maddy wrapped her arms around, led her past the carnival stalls. They took ecstasy, twirled in the fun house mirrors. Cassie smiled at Maddy, "We should just pick the hottest most confident bad bitch version of ourselves and be

that." Maddy found ways to build it stone by stone; Cassie forgot it on the curb when a pretty (useless) boy approached her alone. He offered her a ride in his souped-up truck, fucked her in the bathroom, hand to mouth. Maddy was on the other side, and he had pretended he loved her too. But Cassie's loyalty was the prize and he won. Maddy's friendship didn't

mean anything to her anymore. She primped and preened in the mirror, held lies to her chest—secrets behind a door. Cassie's deception led to self destruction, she let someone who couldn't love dress, and design the perfect identity for her. He liked a softer Maddy clone. Cassie ran like a coward

when the truth burst bright into the open. Maddy demanded answers, but she wouldn't get them, Cassie was so broken— Maddy understood the depth of platonic devotion, promised she would never do that to Cassie. She walked away from white woman tears, a new world set in motion.

Bluebeard's Harem – Marisa Silva-Dunbar (she/her)

I.

He told each of us we were the only one;
would call to us deep in the night like satin.
The seducer, knows how to speak the Devil's tongue,
to turn words on their head so that our minds reeled,
as he whispered in our ears and tied our hands to the bed.

At 3AM he would make a feast of lobster tails soaked
in butter, trace our lips with strawberries, "*Here is the elixir
of love—swallow and we will be tethered in ecstasy.*"
We were overfed. He'd splurge on shopping sprees
at Banana Republic, place AirPods in our palms,
$450 boots for Christmas, a patio heater to keep us warm.

II.

There were murmurs of the others, clues someone
was here *just before*. Echoes just outside the bedroom,
he said they were ghosts—secrets I could not find,
tell me not to look for trouble, though he laid
it right in front of me and never hid it behind a door.

Bluebeard likes to hoard his women, carve each into
a pawn. Some will gladly stay on the shelf, waiting—
addicted to his narcissism, guzzling down his poison,
desiring to be devoured, destroyed in one his rages.

I left when I found the hidden key, tried to get the other
women to follow me—I was the only one to make it beyond
the wilderness, build a home at the edge of the woods,
a cunning witch, warning others of his treachery.

Vorfreude – Marisa Silva-Dunbar (she/her)

I could've loved her more
if she weren't a wanderer.

In summer I'd find her at sunrise
in the grove of citrus trees,
singing with the starlings.

She couldn't belong to me,
and even though she wanted
to tuck me in her pocket—
she couldn't keep me.

Loneliness was the oceans
and galaxies between us.
Her sighs, songs in the wind.
She said she found pieces of me

inscribed in the temples in Rome,
hidden in the markets in Izmir.
She could hear my echoes
in the caverns of Puerto Princesa.

In her final letter, she wrote:
I will follow the sun back to you.

Rapunzel – Emma Wells (she/her)

Familiar spikes prick,
piercing deep
as the depths of souls.

Not yours—
it's shallow
like a baby pool,
frightened of shadow,
quips of fairy-tale legend.

You shake, sway,
buoyed by ineptitude;
swaddled as a newborn,
cushiony-furred;
you hold furls,
prise them close
like your Adam's apple:
it dips in lies,
treacle-thick,
submerging deceit
in choked swallows.

My locks swirl,
are rotating ribbons
dusting untrodden floors
waking to your absence;
my power shifts,
towers then wanes
as moon tide.

I've learnt not to wait.

Glossy gossamers
are dissolvable as bubbles—
existing in chimeras,
where fragments of soul
are ill-fettered:
rustily mangled
as eroding madness.

Ineptitude shrieks, hollers,
neon-luminescent,
as you shrink,
folding to corners
like unwanted house spiders.

My pigtail swats you,
ribboned-gold
as you totter on pins,
unstable shadows.

Cake and Jelly Cream – Mimi Flood (she/her)

I put my two fingers
In a cake
Jelly cream filling oozed out.
I was only 15, when I got down
On my knees for an altar boy who called me ugly.
But he was a total babe, and I wanted to fill a void
That my father left in me.
Every time I laid on a different mattress
I would fall into the springs, cut myself open.
The smell of me would
Make the dogs come,
Sharp fangs to rip me apart,
limb from limb, where I just
Stare at a blank tv screen
And get called lazy, because
It's too loud.
See things and look beyond it.
I'm looking at a flagpole my Uncle hung himself on.
I don't want anyone to really look into me.
I have the manipulation of a cat.
I learned from one of my mother's boyfriends
Late at night.

Pretty Words – Mimi Flood (she/her)

I like pretty words like lilac, blades, and milk.
My hands bound by a rose vine behind my back.
Thirty three kisses of saliva and samples of fingering.
My wrists started to bleed, food for the rose at the end.
Paint for the animal's noses after they tongued the dirt.
Palms smelt like sliced peach chunks.
I am your moonlight and flower garden.
My name is a song that stings your lips.
I'll bite your chapped lips.

A Knife in between my Thighs – Mimi Flood (she/her)

To wear a pretty dress and have a knife
In between my thighs.
Carving my skin with words I am fed with.
I have this craving to move my face like clay into nothing.
I binge on tongues, with blue dildos that feel
Like hot wax that a bee mistakes honey for.
Thorns in my hair.
Pricking hands that make the flower buds grow at the ends.

Inch by second – Sana Mujtaba (she/her)

The chiffon wounds
Yearn for the cure
And under these sheets
The hands explore
the waning melodies of this life
Only to lose at the hands of unwritten insecurities, inch by
second
Let the heart say it out loud

Isn't it enough?
To put a smile on the face of the hostility?
The world is busy searching for fantasy
That is unbeknownst to me
On the precipice of barbarity, a riot whispers in the ear
That the blue sky lost sunbeams
And the voices found it in dreams
Mars cried acid rains on my ambitions

Melting at the edge of the mercury-filled ocean
The kaleidoscopic analogies seem insignificant
As the lungs keep breathing in the
sulphur from pale skin
A vague contentment
And the crusade to win each other lost in silent arguments.

Satellite heart – Sana Mujtaba (she/her)

Lost in the dark embrace of the midnight
I glide with the exhausted hyphens and commas
Navigating through space
The vast expanse of your Ursa major heart is impervious
And the one who kept promises is spinning towards the event
horizon
A catastrophe is flowing from the eyes
Your calming voice is vanquished
Surrendered desperately
The unbecoming singularity
Crimson tidal waves have reached their

apex
And the Orion belt of this life that breathes transgressions is
perpendicularly outrageous
On the cusp of decay, I struggle to stay
in my orbit
My space is poisoned by the anxieties

I slowly misplace myself in the chasms of neutron stars.

Sacrosanct – Emily Perkovich (she/her)

I'm kneeling/sinking/drowning in sand. I always wondered
about the sand. And she's crying, again. She's
barefoot/smoking/crying. Head-in-hands praying. She's always
head-in-hands, and I'm left fingers-in-ears. I'm skeptic-eyes-
rolling. I'm face-turned-skyward, wishing someone would
answer her. But I'm never praying. I said wishing not praying.
I'm kneeling/sinking/drowning in sand. And there's bowls full
of mud. And bowls full of rocks. And bowls filled with tears.
And bowls brimming with grass. And bowls teeming with
berries. And there's bowls filled with tears. And there's bowls
bursting with stars. And this bowl is empty. And I'm adding
everything in pinches and drops. And I'm fingers-in-ears. And
she's mouthful-of-smoke, praying. And maybe if I bless the
tears. Call it makeshift-holy-water. Call it baptism. Call it
sacred. Call the berries wine. Call the rocks body-of-christ. Call
it anointed. Call the mud resurrection. Call it divine. Call me
god-fearing-converted. Call me devout. Call it
wishing/praying/pretending. Call me
kneeling/sinking/drowning. Call it baptism. Give me three
days. Make me a miracle. Make me believe. Make me the
reason. And I'm stirring. And I'm mixing. And I'm wishing. And
she's barefoot/smoking/crying. And I'm waiting. And there's
never any Passover. The firstborn always dies.

Red and Blue (TW) – Alice Carroll (she/her)

We don't want pity
We want the subdued respect that comes with a sort of
practical understanding
Respect for someone who was forced into a fetal position by
steel-toed boots
And the violence that feeds off the pain of tiny defenseless
forms
Because we didn't just fucking get up and walk away
These are the sins of the father
And the age old assumption of eroticism
That twisted men consider an attachment of their ego
Justifying horrors within the vulnerable hierarchy of a family
Was there a glitch the moment I slammed into that concrete
barricade?
Did I tumble into a parallel reality where I hadn't survived?
Straining the threads of existence with an unexpected
determination
Stumbling over lost souls and threading our fingers together
for a heady moment of relief
It often seems like I'm still painfully hovering just above the
surface
Dreaming of a day when they finally fear us

Shared Sickness (TW) – Alice Carroll (she/her)

We all have it.
It's in the angle of the head
The tightening of the jaw
Or a haze contorting your eyesight
It can come to us in dreams even as we soundlessly settle into sleep
Never anticipating the reoccurring horrors as a scream funnels through our chest
We jerk into wakefulness
Still seeing...
While our body remains sodden like damp stone
We all have it.
The triggers that pummel us into a fetal position when
30 seconds ago our priority was an unloaded dishwasher
You've seen it
Maybe it was your reflection
Succumbing to unfettered sobs
Dry heaving our burdens into porcelain therapists
Or the coarse sensation of labored breathing as the world narrows
Jolting awake in a pool of blood streaming from deep rivulets that have made mazes against vulnerable skin
An empty bottle winking in the iridescent light of the one bulb and a blessedly blank memory
Tamping down your initial proclivity that less is better
But he looked like your dad so you absentmindedly stifle the hunger pangs
Feeling your spirit slowly ascend above your head
Lingering
Giving you a moments of respite
Instinctively jerking away from the unassuming touch of a friend

A lover
Because if you've been touched like that by the wrong person,
Sometimes you damn well don't want anyone else's hands against your skin
Because they always seem to feel like his
That fine line between healthy and psychological disintegration
It's seems a wonder that a contorted form can still emit light after swallowing so much shadow
We all have it.
So tell them that it's not their fucking playground
Grave robbers
Vacant cores searching for a host
Searching for veins to drain
A mind to pillage
A hand to grant tremors to
Tell them to go
Every
Single
Fucking
Time
They come back
Tell them to go
Because we all have it.

Firth of Morning – Tom Squitieri (he/him)

There is debate on when best
to discover the beauty of
the firth.
When to enter
When to linger
When to escape
This is no debate
Here
For this very private
Firth of reveal
Firth of morning
The invitation is awake
Again
In harmony the water is calm
The sides of earth majestic and warm
The sky awaiting
The gaze that is the signal
So stand quietly
Now
Flare your imagination
Flicker your energy
Trust me

The Weeping Woman – Tom Squitieri (he/him)

Up through the walkway,
the moans swept
Chilling more than what the raspy wind
with freezing tears had already done
to my body
Shudders sweep me, much like the bitter morning
Had already launched
as memories of La Llorna came
The Weeping Woman whose stories seem to
No longer stay on the waterfront
To mourn
But to insist her anguish
Cries, her moans of sorrow
Haunt us always
everyone, everywhere
Deep in each body part
Yet these moans this morning
teased
Taunted
Tempted
Transfixed
Like the wind that froze all around,
there was no escaping
this cry of rawness.
Wanton trembling
each step continues closer
Closer
For the weeping to emerge
In truer form

As it built
Because, they were
Doing just that
The moans let go of the world
And grasped passion

Car door open
steam following unrestrained legs
outside to the air
Almost fog like
As if on the waterfront
Another moan of passion
Louder,
Of desperate desire
Deep in the car
Penetrating the fierce coldness
Of this impossible hour of the night
That heat pulled me
Against my will
Stirred warmth in subterranean areas
As the spectacle
Burned torridly in an otherwise
hushed church parking lot
Now the moans are clear
As is the couple.
Yet while visible
It is the sounds that elevate the moment
No longer forlorn
Now furious and apodictic
A fuselage of cries and demands and gasps
A skirr shattering the stillness

in a supernatural crescendo
The open door of the car
Inviting me and the
World to reify
Yet we knew that only the fortunate
Could achieve those windswept moans
As they played near dangerous water

Crooked Rockpools – Tiggy Chadwick (she/her)

I started calling myself an orphan
When she died,
So I didn't have to account for the absence of him.

I am all three of us now.
She used to be mother, and she was father.
She didn't like it, and neither do I.

I've been building elaborate rock pools,
In what I think their shapes might be.
And the tide creeps in and fills them.

Parent-shaped people seep into me.
At last, I am held, I am holding.
And then the tide recoils.

I think a lot about skimming all
Those rocks away, off into the night.
I might become the naked sand.

What I do instead is, damn these pools,
So no water can get in.
I use the litter that the tourists leave behind.

Everyone leaves something behind
And it was me this time, me and the sea.
I got left behind.

I'm unsure what to do with myself.

It's me, the sea.
Et c'est l'appel du vide.

I sometimes just sit with them
Right in the middle,
Within them and without them.

I should fit here, I think.
I wish I did, I don't though,
I'm cold and awkwardly shaped,

I'm all knees and elbows,
Cramming myself in where I'm not wanted.
I am a spectacle.

I'd like to disappear completely.
Be the sand and fall away
In sheets with the tide.

I slip away in small moments, like they did,
At night, with no witnesses.
I sip at the sea.

These tourists have all got me
Under their fingernails, between their toes,
And they aren't shaking me off.

I've gotten into all these small places now
But I want to be here,
With my rock pools by the water.

I long to be not part of the sea,
But to be a daughter,
I want to be somebody's daughter.

I'm not a rock pool,
Or the shore, or a daughter,
But I am like them, an alcoholic.

You see, the sea has already started!
It sinks its fingers into me,
And it pulls away handfuls.

I'm not falling away like the shoreline,
Like I thought I might,
Like I thought they did.

No, I'm being ripped apart,
And I didn't even notice!
Until I started to resemble them.

I look so tired,
So withered, and tired...
I am so unbelievably tired!

I haven't slept through the night,
In so long, I haven't had time to eat,
I can hardly hear myself think these days.

To be your own parents
You must become them,
And that's exactly what I did.

Life Isn't Enough When You Have Time – adam Shove
(he/him)
This was a silver medal,

Flowers wasted with the colours on their petals.

Sit back down,

Emotional ideas have become quite

Disposable to you.

This was the new process.

Pushing the lungs and the fragile heart,

Citron tart, young caffeine beans.

Blonde sun within the land of sunshine,

Given security with byzantine.

Life isn't enough when you have time.

Heretics instrumental me,

Not the ideal map of a family tree.

Orthodox talking within an equinox,

Do you remember being happy?

Can you taste your own evidence,

Or is this even a thing.

The bull and hunters forever in the night sky,

If the world is flat,

Then explain the rotation of water.

You were drunk and the poison was porter,

I was listening to

The stale music in a room;

Sounding like a coffin,

Promising myself to never become maudlin.

I was back at the Mausoleum walls,

Qualified into words becoming prophesied,

Not my words,

Who could handle my words?

Faucet Salt – adam Shove (he/him)

I didn't know if an idea

Should stop at a point,

Or reevaluate itself

With regards to an Escher painting Relativity

On a light switch.

A better explanation on a state of survival

Found in a non-syncopated pattern,

Amputated actions happen

Within the heavy weather.

Nadir could have been upwards,

If I had a sense of direction.

Correction,

If only I cared for my own geolocation.

What three words?

Unsure availability here.

Dogs that roam a coffee shop,

Slowed down remix of Iggy Pop.

Faucet salt and when you mix that

With how I learnt not to care about the world,

I guess that became

All the answers I ever gave;

Between the convalescing scars

And the blue lightning bolt.

A love letter to my younger self – Lilith Kerr (she/they)

Dear 17 year old me, put down the knife. Put down the pills and the bottle of bleach. I wish I could wrap you in my arms, tell you that this isn't your forever; that you're going to walk—and sometimes claw—your way back from the edge of the cliff. One day, you're going to be able to look at a blade and not burn up with hunger.

Dear 18 year old me, you're feeling anger spill into you for the first time—feeling it bite the edges of your vision a gruesome red. I know the way guilt floods through you. I know you're afraid to show anything but that practiced grin that slicks your mouth like a knife. It's okay, you're going to learn to accept the rage; to greet it on even ground and carry it in your gut, pulsating and spectacular.

Dear 19 year old me, you cut your tongue again and again on the edges of her name, syllables sliding past teeth dulled from use. When are you going to stop splintering yourself against the floor, begging someone to love the fragments? I want to tell you to lower yourself down from that pike. Grit your teeth. The sacrificial lamb never gets the girl, and the slaughter never did you any good, anyway.

Rage // Nurture – Lilith Kerr (she/they)

I pluck the rage from my chest

And give it space to grieve;

To scream itself hoarse.

I love you still,

Even in this wrecked state of mind.

But I feel myself growing around that same love,

The way a tree learns to bend itself around steel,

The way a dormant seed brings itself to life.

I am changing;

Unbecoming and remaking myself

With gentle hands.

Think body unbowing from the earth.
Think hair blooming gold in lucid air.

Everyday, I sat with hope, hot and heavy, in my palms.

And every night, I found my fingers singed with desire.

I longed for you to plunge

Into soil and drag me from my crypt.

But you were never one to get your hands dirty, were you?

So now I am the necromancer in this story

/ a forest fire raging itself to death / roots like teeth
sinking into dirt / trees bearing bitter fruit / I can
swallow my own beating heart;
I can kiss my lungs back to breath.

I have lived half-alive for far too long

And now I'm bringing myself back from the grave.

—but not for you

I can't go back to Pittsburgh — Amanda Brown (she/her)

because just the thought of that city
makes me nauseous. I couldn't listen
to Grayscale for months after that trip
without wanting to puke because while
they played on stage, I stood in the back
of the crowd, my abdomen on fire and
my mind tormented with blood and loss.

We didn't lose the baby. *I* didn't lose
the baby. But we spent the rest of that cold
wet night in the ER getting ultrasounds
and MRIs and zero answers for the pain
tearing me in half at 12 weeks. We didn't
lose the baby, but we lost a little bit of us
on the 10-hour drive back to St. Louis.
I whimpered with every bump
and took Tylenol every 4 hours
just to make the pain bearable.

We didn't do much sightseeing,
and I'm sure Pittsburgh is lovely
in October. But I can't even think
of the city without feeling sick
with the reminder of our almost-loss
and everything we did lose.

After 20 Hours of Labor, My Baby is Ready to Be Born, But We have to Wait – Amanda Brown (she/her)

I had to stop pushing—more than
once—because the doctor wasn't there
yet. The head was crowning
and the nurse and my husband debated

the baby's hair color—brown
like his or blonde like mine?—as I tried
to resist my body's natural urge

to just push the thing out already
because even with two epidurals,
I was uncomfortable. But the nurse
assured us the baby would arrive
before midnight. By the time

the doctor showed, it was after
eleven. She moved in slow motion
as she said I could push. I inhaled

then exhaled as I pushed, and the oxygen
mask pushed up under my eyes each time.
And then my son was born and my husband
cut the cord that was wrapped twice around

the baby's neck. I delivered the placenta
and got stitched up—just a few, the doctor
said—and a nurse put the baby on my chest.

I wanted to cry, but couldn't, so I grimaced
instead. We still weren't sure about
the baby's hair color.

Untitled – Courtney Written (she/her)

The glass I touch is fragile,

Or it could be

I don't test its strength

Instead I admire it's clear beauty

I can see through it

It doesn't seem to be hiding anything,

But why would it be?

I bet it knows it's still a work of art

If it cracks, breaks, or shatters

It would just be harder to get close to,

Sharp edges are painful, hard to ignore

Recognizing what happened can be a chore,

Still, how it got that way matters

Inheritance – Jordan Nishkian (she/her)

My grandmother was a great cook.
Because of that,
a crumple of tinfoil in the freezer
holds the last thing I have
from her hands.

Her cheese borag recipe:
- 1 package frozen phyllo dough, thawed
- 1 pound jack cheese, shredded
- 2 cubes butter (salted), melted
- 1 large egg, beaten

She stopped putting parsley in them
when my dad stopped
liking green—one of those sacred
traditions that only changes
for youngest sons;

one of those simple traditions
(inherent, dreamlike),
that the hands of eldest daughters
keep when the mind draws
a blank—

She clears the counter (except
for bowls of water and butter, a greased pan)
and unfolds sheets of pastry,
cutting it into thick strips,
"Don't drag the knife, it'll tear."

She dips her fingers in water and pulls
apart the stack by ply,

brushing each with butter,
"Don't press, it'll tear."

She spoons the filling on the end, edges meet
and fold into a triangular parcel,
"Don't overstuff, it'll tear."
Top with extra butter and bake—
350°, hotter? 10 minutes, longer?
"Don't think, it'll tear."
—until the phyllo flakes and
butter pools and browns.

She knew she was dying two days
before the virus put her
lungs in the hospital,
before I saw sparse notes and blanks
on her recipe cards.

Aluminum gleans in the frostbite.
Cold air swaddles my face
as I close the freezer door.

The story of two breakdowns – Jordan Nishkian (she/her)

The first: a forest green Jeep I named Matilda.
Mileage dialing 280,527, the cabin lights flickered
when I opened my door; cracked leather seats revealed

yolk-colored cushion. Rain leaked through the roof—
forgotten since California's drought—the cd player
spit discs at me if I went over a speed bump too fast.

Matilda was mechanically sound, except she would cut
her engine (mostly in the Starbucks drive-thru and
side streets during my commute through Costa Mesa).

Dashboard dials dipping in erratic tempos, radio off,
the low, hearty rumble of her body would die. I could
revive her, haunted by visions of her spiting me

in the thick of 405 traffic. Monday, after Matilda
cut her engine three days in a row, I took her to Ralph.
He said that a car's issues become more exacerbated

with age. My mom, a caregiver, called this
becoming *more-so*. Ralph said he'd look, but
couldn't help unless it happened in front of him.

The second: my roommate Shira.
She never used the kitchen, I only heard her
in passing—it was hard to recognize her voice

when she called for me Wednesday morning.
Hot tea in hand, I knocked, asking, *Are you ok?*
Her cracked voice said something was wrong—

Help—her door was locked, she couldn't get up.
I rested my tea in the corner and ran my hand on top
of the doorframe till I found the dust-covered key pin.

Lock unlatched, I pushed the door to see Shira
balled up on her mattress, gripping the middle of her back
like the outline of a bird. *Should I call someone?*

911? Her head bobs, eyes and teeth clamped tight:
Can you take me? Ralph's voicemail said he couldn't get
Matilda to not work (not even in the Starbucks drive-thru).

With her arm draped over my neck and both our purses
Slung over my shoulder, we hobbled out the door
to Shira's 1999 Corolla. By eleven, she got painkillers

and a bed. *Can you stay with me? —Yes.*
I propped my phone on the overbed table so we
could watch Friends. After hours, tests, laugh tracks,

we learned her untreated kidney infection
turned septic, was spreading, she'd need
to be hospitalized. *We're going to do everything*

we can, her doctor said, eyes cemented to
her chart. *But she'll be here for a few days.*
Between episodes, nurses, conversations, Shira cried

for the inconveniences, calling me Monica. She
drifted off while we watched The One With the Tea Leaves.
I took the keys to her Corolla to grab a few things from home.

(Shira named her car Winona). Ralph called on the way:
Your car is working fine. I'm doing everything

I can. You should pick it up tomorrow.

The apartment's
quiet wasn't unusual—but my thoughts were loud.
I found a duffle bag in her closet and packed her pillow,
a lumpy bear, the throw blanket with a rip in the stitching.

Closing her door behind me, I spotted the mug left
in the corner. On my way out, I walked my cold tea to
the sink, wondering how my car had made itself better.

The common heritage of all our awkward bodies//Of mice, machines, and miracles//Thank you for making me feel welcome in the world – Sascha Felix Luinenburg (he/they)

How can they coexist,
The periscope
And the little sea snake,
Its head held just above water,
From which it was conceived?

The stealth bomber
Fertilizing sterile cities with fire
And the white bird wheeling
Silently in a sky too still
For mind to abide?

We with the mountains and the sun
A chip in a white, china cup?

The garden and the homeless gardener?

This unkempt bush under the trees,
Its soft moss and bramble tangle of centuries
You can't imagine cropping back
Into anything.

These fields are a pair of old cupped hands, and we
The brackish water
Slipping from their fingers.

You gather dead mice: you work
In the sweat of your brow
At the task of extracting
A life from vast life.

Thinking of gasoline cans
and particles of plastic degrading and fake lashes
I lay my odd, knotted head against my knees in shame,
An affected likeness of ageing willows resigning their balding
branches
To twitch and wrestle with stars and tiny comet fish vanishing
And with wind and roots in green water.

We doubt whether we ought
To drink from the yellowing spring
That waters all this land.
I hope that when I'll sleep
I won't have to cough quite so much.
We are tired. Always tired. But,
Amid bumbling doubts, whistling and whispering
Field self-recriminating and reversing
In the breeze, dear queer innocence, ever-
Present friend, you kiss my ear
With the wallop of a sudden storm.

Cinder Girl Grows Wings – Stephanie Parent (she/her)

Maybe fairy tales were my first kink.
The ultimate tease and denial:

Sleep in ashes and sweep enough floors
and you, too, will win princes and wealth.
So said Disney and the Brothers Grimm, in
their different palettes. Technicolor or
chiaroscuro, I devoured them
indiscriminately. My fetishes
whittled down to the finest
intricacies:

The jagged pink spikes of Cinderella's
dress, after her sisters got their hands
on it, on her. Her hopes more beautiful
for being torn.

The glowing tip of a spindle, perilous
and lovely. Sharp enough to penetrate
my flesh and, deeper still, my
dreams.

The precise details of a story—
three drops of blood spilled
from an ebony window onto white
snow. Not two, not four—
Exactly. Three.

Fairy tales offered the steps of a spell: a
story of sacrifice and pain, a vow of
witness and rescue, a Dom cradling
their cane-striped, shaking sub after

a scene. The fantasy promising fulfillment
that never quite lasted, always danced,
a shimmering enchantment, just beyond
my reach.

Until I found myself older, awakening
alone in ashes, disillusioned, throat
coated with soot and eyes tearing
against the sting.

Only so long could I
suffer for a dream.

I turned to a different genre of stories,
a different kind of kink. Tales of
winged creatures rising from ashes,
a fetish for transformation, a firebird
burning my love for my own pain
away.

No more waiting among the cinders
for someone to listen, to save me, to see.
Just me, sending my stories of strange desires
out into the universe, another sort of
exhibitionism, soaring on fiery
wings.

Blessed Curse – Stephanie Parent (she/her)

Dear, you were blessed:
The beloved daughter your parents wished for
For so long

Dear, you were cursed:
With your birth, your seven brothers
Lost their human forms

(your fault, your fault, your fault)

Dear, you were blessed:
The good stars gave you a gift
To unlock castle doors

Dear, you were cursed:
You lost the good stars' gift
And surrendered your own finger bone

(your pain, your pain, your pain)

Dear, you were blessed:
The glass castle shattered
A frosted illusion, brought down by
Your sacrifice, your blood

Dear, you were cursed:
Your brothers were restored
But you remained the girl whose life
Had never been her own

(your love, your love, your love)

Dear, you were cursed:
No prince waited, tall and strong among the glass shards
To mourn over your missing finger, order a replacement
Made of precious metal, weld you whole

Dear, you were blessed:
You gazed at the stump on your left
Hand, a hole gutted from your
Heart, made visible to all

You said

(*I'm whole, I'm whole, I'm whole*)

Watch Hill Park – Rhys Campbell (he/him)

Nestled away next to John Smith's Bay,
Lies the geographical embodiment of peace.
You'll feel the stresses you carry decrease
And the wonders of the world come out to play.

It is visible when fleeting down the windy road,
Hidden when the eyes peek at the ocean,
The endless blanket of undulating Bondi blue.

If you take a moment to sit on the rocks,
Close your eyes and get lost,
This is when you'll discover
This is the centre of the universe,
The physical channel to the astral plane.

Listening to the universe perorate,
Voices of wisdom to attain,
I snap back to the physical plane,
This physical vessel
With a calmness I maintain.

Spectating the endless ocean bed,
The sounds of calmly crashing waves
Against the rock face,
The present moment I embrace.

This Heart Holds Only Grief (a series of drafts) – Robin Williams (she/they)

- My grandmother died and just like my thoughts, I can't form a complete poem

- How do you grieve a grandparent's death while grieving the absence of your parents who are grieving their parent's death?

- I grew up the day my grandmother died / I became an adult the day my grandmother died

- I have one picture in my phone and she's not even looking at the camera but at least two pictures of him because he was supposed to go first.

- You're dead and I'm not sure how to wrap my head around this confusion

- I was painting you a card on Saturday night when I heard the phone ring and silence when dad picked it up. I was painting the first blue sky when dad came down the stairs and stood in the corner of the living room. I was painting a moon, a part of me deep inside knew you'd never see again, but it wasn't until dad said, "She just died," that it occurred to me that maybe I didn't want to see the moon again. We were supposed to see you on Sunday. I was supposed to see you. I wanted to see you. I wanted to give a thousand apologies with my eyes for being mad all those years you and Poppy stayed silent when a simple phone call would have been nice. I wanted to say thank you for the card but thank you for more than that, thank you for trying to tie up loose ends even if it was only for a selfish matter, but I can't say anything to you now.

I don't know if it's the regret or the grief or my menstrual cycle, but everything reminds me of you and everything hurts because of it.

I TOOK MY CAT TO THE VET AND THE WORLD REMINDS ME OF EVERYTHING I'M MISSING – Robin Williams (she/they)

I walk down the stairs expecting to round the corner to see his face and bury my fingers in the fur on his neck, but he isn't there and I feel hollow inside just like I did when

My first cat laid in the bookshelf cube and cried, and I foolishly thought it was for attention, until I got there and looked into his sorry eyes to notice he was hurting and I

tried to give him water, and treats, and held his tiny paws but he still let out a last breath and died. My sister tried to give him CPR, every time his lifeless muscles twitched like they would in sleep, like

Boots, who falls off window ledges and has eight lives left in her energetic bones, after she tangled her leash tight around her throat, laying limp in my arms as I screamed for my Father

who took her from me, when I dropped to my knees, and spoke life into her again. She shuts her eyes on the way to the hospital, twitches and goes limp in her sleep, still breathing, and I'm reminded of the nightmares of when their chests stopped rising.

RUST – Basil (they/them)

Beloved

I

On a quiet and bleak morning of early July, the sky turned into a crimson-sapphire mixture. Horde of animals—birds, reptiles, canines, rodents, all blood hungry flooded the streets. A terrifying sight. When a man shook out of his reverie and saw a disembodied figure spread out on the floor. A knife in his hand. Around his bare feet the steel-blue and oxblood coalesce from his tears and the rotten thing he had slaughtered ripples away slowly, taking its time. Tattered and delirious, the man rocks back and forth with his hands and knees on the floor. The blood pools below his eyes and the reflection he sees in it renders him wide-eyed and hypnotized. *Violet, my Beloved,* he whispers and the song comes next, clear and loud in his dreadful jail.

take me where moonflowers bloom
find me a soft melody
like a distant memory
of you my beloved
my beloved, my beloved

He weeps, remembering everything that came before madness seized him. The song carries on.

I'd have stopped the blood
and turned back time

for my beloved
but I've learnt that there are
stronger things than my love
and no love would have won this battle
no love that isn't yours and mine
you must understand
I had to be the sacrifice

II

. My beloved, she is an undulating bloom.
A million sunflowers opening up at once.
Radiant and filled with promises.
I shudder under the weight of her aquamarine
eyes on mine: firm and unrelenting
in a way I've never been gazed at.

She sees past my body and doesn't call
me a fraud for stealing it.
She tells me that the body is a mere vessel
and it's the soul who's holy.
Because holy things must be venerated, she gives
me her heart and I devote to her

Nauseated and defeated, I lean into the window
and see the sky in its scarlet-azure blend.
The train moves swiftly but I feel the sea
far away, unforgiving and unattainable.
I turn to my palm hoping to see a glimpse of

my beloved or to know whether the beating thing
she kept there still beats. I hear her singing.

my beloved, my beloved
take my picture
hold me inside your palm
keep me closer than time

There is no time left for us. Everything is uprooted.
They took me from my beloved. An abomination—
they called me, and locked me away from my beloved.

III

When it rains it's a marvelous sight.
Lapis lazuli—thousands of them cascade down splitting the
ground with carmine glow.
My rage transports rapidly. The sky howls with my anguish.
Everyone is scrambling to find shelter from red-eyed death
and the mad man walking among them.
The sea, cobalt blue and possibly nursing my beloved, stares
back at me. I hear the song and everything stills.

my beloved, my precious ruby
this is all I could do
so don't hate me for leaving
my beloved, my beloved
do you reckon I'll go to heaven?

The waves roar and the wind cradles a soft voice. Cerulean

meets vermilion and it becomes loss. He hears it and knows in his heart that it's the last of his beloved he'll ever see.

no love that isn't mine and yours
shall bloom in my heart
and no heart that isn't held by your hands shall beat in my chest
my beloved, my beloved
do you reckon we'll go to heaven?

He grips the beating thing, now subdued, and the sea welcomes him.
Open up! Take me to my beloved
Take me! body and soul
unfit and mismatched, he yells at the sea.

The sea rocks him in its belly.
Red drops into the deep blue water & everything is transformed. He hears the song one last time and knows in his heart that there's no place built for them.

my beloved, my beloved
do you reckon we'll love in heaven?

Dust

I didn't know before that moment how permanence could be
beaten down into smaller parts. Into nothing. A voice in an

empty house. A weeping child left alone. A love hunched
before guillotine and seeing its lover holding the rope. I am

a piece within a dream woven by tar blood threads, thick and
foul, into something real and trembling. Ready to fix

itself. To make pretty its own marred skin. For a second
chance or for anyone willing to hold it close.

Close enough
to be rendered soft again.

You saw a monster with prominent yellow eyes. Mouth torn
open by its own teeth, black mud stuck at their sharp ends.

Its skin stitched together in hideous patches, almost peeling
off entirely. You saw it and kept your gaze. When you touched

its most vulnerable part, you softened its mouth, smoothed its
skin and bestowed tenderness into its unloveable hands.

You made *him.* A permanent change, the beast
(now tender and naive) believed.

You turn to him one day, as if seeing him for the first time. You hold his gaze till you flinch away sick from whatever

you found in his face and body. His mouth keeps disfiguring at
a quick speed. Turning flesh in and out. He keeps saying
sorry because it takes a lot of restraint to keep certain things
hidden and your pale eyes rocked him out from his hold.

You are curled into your knees with both hands clutching
the sides of your head. You don't hear his apology.

I'm crumbled and difficult to look at.
My only comfort comes from the wind
that carries me along with dirt.

Death, metaphorically

Can I borrow a sunflower?
My mother's birthday is almost over, you see, and I must give
her something lovely

She's thirty years older than me and we share the same
Tiredness. Defeat.

I'm as generous as one could get with my tears, I feed them
every couple of hours
It's six thirty and I have fed them just thirty minutes ago

October—my time of the year

Fire rears cold, all colors look
calm in my eyes

In my eyes the world is a giant pot
My life began as the sizzle of oil
in a much smaller one

A little bird rests at my windowsill
quiet, blue, and gentle. A life well lived, growing into
something old and peaceful

A sentiment I had once embodied before this defeat.
My mother's stooping shoulders
remind me of everything I could never have
All the wonder gone from my soul's bright summer glow
Did you know God sends birds to his favorite ones?
I hear its voice occasionally—my wayward soul
It's faint, but it sings
The stars will bring me back to you

I don't believe in god. Not anymore
The confession comes out with a choke, almost as if a part of
me still

wants to hold onto him or perhaps that's god's touch
god doesn't like losing
his favorite ones, so I've heard

I always knew I was my mother's favorite one because she was
most tender with me
How tender our affairs seem in the eye of cosmos

Do stars look at us and weep?
Do they weep because it takes eternity to deliver the truth to
us—that our love is futile and our

pain is only ours to nurture
Not time's task nor god's test
I have thirty sunflowers in my arms, the florists have

been generous, I'm weeping.
Fire lurks close by, breathing, waiting for its turn
A formidable itch forms itself

I tend to it. I tear. I burn. I weep.
Joy suffocates me as if I were its cherubic child
Every molecule inside me blooms

I never told my mom that I loved her before and I try to
remember, as she greets me with the same rueful smile
and a soft thank you, if I had once truly
loved her
Happy birthday, mom. Goodnight.

The night follows me.

Warm and reliable in its permanent company
I remember loving it once—the night, among other things

I remember loving many things before
None of them tether me to this world the same way ruin does

Daughter of Bones – Emily Perina (she/her)

I was the Daughter of Wands
Head held high, future unknown
How presumptuous to assume we are not like the tiny
plastic toys from quarter machines outside our favorite
bodegas
We get what we get
But don't we always get upset?
Rubber Halloween rats make me nostalgic
Swirling down the bathtub drain
It's the sharp ring of metal, screeching, soothing
Uncompromising
My bounty of the forest has been revealed
Muskrat skull, stuffed with leaves
Hollow eyes
If I could just go back to that moment to take better note of
the how the light shined off the water
How my Father carried the dirt covered creature home
Instructing me to save this fragile reminder
Things do end
I've spent countless hours picking cat
whiskers out of every carpet I've had
Did I really think I would notice the
beginning of mourning my youth?
I am just a moment
A body's memory of another time
Another home
A dead hermit crab with a shell perfectly spiraled
I am the Daughter of Bones

Untitled – Emily Perina (she/her)

My phone lights up, the screen reminds me to drink water
I ignore it like I always do
There is only so much help I can try to give myself before I
cannot stand self love
A breeze pulls through my window screen, ripped by small
claws, holes for flying creatures to come inside attracted to
the light
Watching my cat, watch the outside cats
We are all inside cats now
How have we met in this place
How have we combined
Meteor showers above my head "I own a gun, I hope that is
okay"
This is not my future but what neighborhood will be safe for
me to walk home alone at night
Shadows cavorting in my mind, people of possibilities

My phone lights up, the screen reminds me to drink water

I turn the tap on.

Addicted – Sara Sabharwal (she/her)

I want to do all the things we said we'd do. If time hadn't cheated us. Cut us short. Dead on arrival. A car crash of lust, emotion, rawness. Something you couldn't look away from, as it seared itself into your brain. A new scar. A memory that pulsates through your entire body when the smallest reminder triggers the endorphin rush. A needle in the arm. One more time. One LAST time, then I'll quit you. Stop digging up our grave, chasing ghosts through darkened alleys at ungodly hours. Trying to find remnants of us in the eyes of strangers. I will finally exorcise you from me. Dip my feet in the holy water and taste sunshine.

Maybe.

Just one more time

Secrets & Sins – Sara Sabharwal (she/her)

In the bedside drawer
Merely inches from me
Were the love letters she signed
With hearts in pink ink.
While I signed mine with my teeth,
Fingernails gripping into skin.
Flames of passion wrapped in sin.
Moonlight faded into sunshine
And I wondered which one of us
Was on his mind

Forgiveness has Eight Wobbly Legs – Tyler Hurula (she/her)

The couch had bruised
brushstroke stripes—purple
and a violent shade of rust,

crisscrossed as if punching
each other. Dad reached his roaring

hands around it and flipped
it upside down. It wobbled like a dead
bug twitching. Like the spider

I was too scared to smoosh
so I sprayed it with Windex over

and over until it crinkled
itself into a tiny tremble.
I really didn't want to hurt

something so much smaller than me.
Maybe that's why the couch landed

on the other side of the room.
Earlier that week a baby bird had fallen
from the rafters at my horse riding

lesson. Dad took off his own
shirt, and with a gentle

hand scooped this bald bird
up, and I carried it home on my lap.
The car crawled home to avoid any bumps

for this hollow-boned creature.
His strong and precise hands built

a makeshift nest and we did our best
to nurture it back to health. Both
our eyes spilled over as he laid

the bird in a shoebox coffin,
tucked it in under his shirt.

So, when I look back and ask myself
how I forgave him over and over
and over I remember his hands—

how they threw couches, yes,
and cradled dying birds, too.

So Mad He Can't See Straight – Tyler Hurula (she/her)

Daddy tramples into the kitchen—
eyes bright, ablaze with accusations aiming
outward. I'm caught in the crosshairs.

There are two ways out
but we've already locked
eyes. He's loaded, though
I have yet to see the inside of a bottle.

He looks at me as my eyes leak
and tells me I have cat-shit
green eyes, and if I don't stop, he'll give

me something to cry about.
He's so mad he can't see straight,
and then he doesn't. His eyes go cross,
like the time I rolled mine and he

said they'd stick like that—but his
stick like that.
When my baby sister is born, he hates her

crying because she seems
to do it most when he is in the room.
He holds her tight, like one of those
keychains you squeeze and the eyes

pop out. My mom begs him
to let her go. As his anger grows,
so do his arms. They grow

and grow like they're being

squeezed and my sister slips
out and his arms are too big to hold
her. Dad crouches

with his still crossed
eyes in front of me and my sister.
The closet door came off

its hinges and he wants to know
who did it. My hands are the jello
in the fridge. Tremble seeps
through me as I eye the wooden

spoon splayed out in the pound
of his hands. His jaw juts,
incisors bared like a challenge.

His bottom teeth lengthen
into a lilac lattice fence,
and I paint pink pansies on it.
Fragile wings confetti

the hallway after he slingshot
the tv remote at my mom's
glass angel collection.

She tells me later she read
abusers don't actually lose
control. You can tell because
nothing he ever breaks is his

own. That night when his eyes bleed
clear apologies, I trace the lines
of his hands and watch the

hairs on his knuckles grow
thick and soft as they fleece
into teddy bear paws.
I tell him I have a girlfriend

when he asks if I've found
a boy at college yet. I see red rage
splotch in as he looks past

me in two different directions.
I guess I broke the closet
door on my way out after all,
and he hasn't forgotten. He raises

his oversized arms above his head
and his whole body inflates
with heat until he glitters

into a cloud of dust. The only thing left
is my footprints leading out the door.

To the Man on the Dating App Who Doesn't Understand Why I Didn't Reply Because I'm Fat and Polyamorous – Tyler Hurula (she/her)

My body is the least interesting
thing about me.

As if my soft is a safety net
for you to jump into—no
thank you. My soft is where

love finds me and spreads
out over toast with my wife

each morning. It's where I collect
kisses, wishes, and butterflies

on every first date. It's where
my girlfriend or boyfriend

or joyfriend all congregate
to feast on the abundance

of my honeyed heart.
Being poly does not mean

I'm down to fuck every man,
minisculed by his narrow
view on what he thinks

women want—and I guarantee
that you are not
what we want.

Being poly means
I am picky about who I let undress

me—strip me down and caress
the soft edges of the most interesting

thing about me. Which is not
my body. It is the way I sway

as I play piano and sing the wrong
lines because I never know the right

ones. It is the way I make myself
laugh harder than anyone else

can. It is that I love hard as I fuck,
and I create earthquakes.

Insulting me won't make
my standards limbo to match
the stature of your deflated ego,

and hell yes, I am sexy, and I know
I'm not the only one that thinks so.

You said you hope I end
up alone, and I assure you

I am a kissing
booth and there is a line

limousined down the street,
and your ticket has been rejected.

Ramshackle Skeleton – Asher Phoenix (she/her)

I look in the mirror, a reflection of me staring back at me. Wait

no...it's not me

Too many emotions...

Who is this?

Who the fuck is this staring back at me

Frozen...

Tears fall down like a rainstorm

{{CRACK}}

Ripples of shattered fragments descend

Skeleton fragments floating in total darkness

{{FREEZE}}

Loneliness in the brown irises

Heart chambers beat of pain

Daggers in the back

Mind loud like thunder

Anger spins like a hurricane in the pit of my stomach

Whispers of her voice

"Ash"

Don't search, she's gone...don't fucking search
Flickers of bad dreams

Subconscious the trickster of the mind

I look in the mirror, a reflection of me staring back at me. Wait

no...it's not me

So many emotions...

Who is this?

Who the fuck is this staring back at me

{{FAINT BUZZING}}

Wake up...WAKE UP

Sad sound waves echoed off the mirror

"I'm broken...and I don't know...how to fix me..."

Dark Halo – Asher Phoenix (she/her)

Taking my first breath into this world
I wore a halo of gold
I've always had that cute innocent look
A smile bigger than ever
Had an attitude like a rebel
Ready to aim and fire
I needed to be my own leader
Before anyone could rule me
Before anyone could hurt me
There are devils out there
Disguised as angels
You see...
I wore a halo of gold
So I tried my very best
Except if you look closer
You'll notice I'm wearing
A halo of shadows
Respect your elders
Was sketched in my brain early
So I obeyed that rule
As well as I could
That's until...
I was ripped from the arms of an angel Into
the house of horrors
I hated that house
I hated that bed
I hated that blanket
I hated the food
I hated the clothes

I hated the atmosphere
I hated that woman
Who was the fucking devil
She put on a great performance
When my social worker came knocking
I didn't understand at the time
Why she didn't notice my unhappiness Why
she didn't notice
When I asked about my angel
Or when I tried to ask to go home This
wasn't my home
I'm dead living here
My halo wasn't gold anymore Now
it is vintage with thorns
It holds the devil's whispers
That has no face
But holds flashbacks
Like an old 80's horror movie
I only get one halo
Til this day...
I wear a halo of shadows

Grandfather – Joe Espinoza (he/him)

I inhale
My grandfather's
Wool sweater
And instantly I am
At my first trip
To the sea
Years and years ago
He and I
This man
Who was not a man
But a planet
With many a moon
Cozy in their orbit
Including me
And the aperture
Of my soul was at once and forever open
And my mind seemed not
But the fronds of a plant
Thirsting for the knowledge
Of all the suns

Comfort – Pop (she/her)

There is comfort in heaviness
the weight that envelops my aching
shaking body.

There is comfort in weariness
like an armour that develops
born from anger and self-pity.

There is comfort in heaviness,
the anchor which holds you down
and nails you to the ground.

There is comfort in emptiness,
the numbing of your senses
echoing that of your feelings.

There is comfort in heaviness,
like an excuse you've over-used
thread-bare.

There is comfort in soreness
the slow yet cruel burn reminding
you to keep moving.

The old house – Pop (she/her)

There's an old rusty mirror
between the gracious wooden doors
There's a sunbeam piercing through the glazed window
and dust flying from wall to wall

There's a high, ancient bookshelf
lined with leather-bound tomes
that speak of dark mixtures and metamorphosis
of lost cities and of crying angels

There's a worn-down, tattered rug
whose colours the years have long since stolen
taken away by softly padding feet
and the forgotten whispers of those who couldn't sleep

There's a grand marble staircase
smoothed and polished by many an entrance
where the sway of silken gowns
echoed as loud as waves crashing upon a shore

There's a crackling fire in the kitchen's chimney
warm and loud and swishing rapidly
it sings of freezing winter nights
and growls under a pot of hot water for tea

There's a waning bouquet of lilies and daisies
in a delicate china vase
upon an ottoman of oakwood and jersey
a drop of time that never stays.

Sometimes all you want is to be saved – Ishita Ganguly
(she/her)

Dry leaves of December before falling down
hopes to cling to the branches a little longer,
Forgotten memories want to be recalled
if only for once.
Tears that have dried up
desired if they were but a smile.
The lover who said, "I don't want anything in return,"
Has expected a fair exchange in his solitude.
Deep down the courageous
wants a pat on the back,
The protector wants to be protected.
Even the brain secretly wishes to be conquered by the heart—
Sometimes all you want is to be saved.

To a Conflicted Catholic Lesbian, From a Trans Girl – Mia-Jo Feeley (she/her)

1: What you did

You arrived on the shores of my body like a conquistador.
Equipped & able to explore the mountains of my spine to the
equator of my waist:
   to dump platinum in the ocean for not being gold.
   to give the natives diseases.
        to give the survivors your church.
        to abandon the children you had with them &
   to judge them when they peel the skin off a saint
          & take her cadaverous blessing
          because, yes, you also gave them your
cisnormativity.

2: What you actually did, aka Rules for the Next Love

You shall not have me in your prayers & your confessions.
You shall not treat me like your boyfriend; put your hands on
my hips when we dance.
You shall not project your peoples' problems onto the penis—

        the innocent phallus which these days I see as
feminine
        not as a contrarian but as a sincerely sinful
heretic.
        Yes, I am genuine, I think they're cute,
I hate to focus on aesthetics without theology but this *is*
Catholicism.

3: Your Questions

You say you are uncertain
about the love of God
but you don't commune with me either
& yes I believe everything is divine
but what that means to you
means violence for me, my exes, my girls, my
sisters, & my people—
our thoughts have consequences.

4: My Questions

If bread can be Jesus, can't I be your girl?
Does the apple in my throat put you off?
Did you not notice it before or did you not expect to
get this far
without Judgement for loving a girl?
How do you feel about yourself?
Does He let you love yourself despite being a
girl?
Or are you a pillar of salt?
Did not woman come of man?
How better could I fit your parent's book?
You know it says nothing about girls kissing?
It's Eve's apple. It's Eve's serpent.

5: I'm Not Heartbroken I'm Just Angry & Heartbroken

Charm is deceitful, beauty is vain, but a woman who loves the
LORD
    is to be maimed in her own bed for she should
    be only afraid.
Go & confess what you did to me & how it felt,
    but my god thinks I'm pretty
    & I use her name in vain.
What is a name but something to whisper,
     to moan,
     to search for in a Potter's Field,
     to remember,
     to wear even when it's too big so you
     eat & eat
     & hope you grow into it?

6: What I'm Really Upset About

In the history of imperial plagues,
From Antonine to Smallpox to Typhus to St. Covid XIX,
the laws they brought to the new world must be the most
rampant.
This parasitic virus fused to our genome,
& made code that said:
"There is among the pagans much sodomy, sharing their filth
& dressing as women."
    &
"There's only room for one spirit in a body, & they always
match."
    &

"Male & female He created them, & also Earth is the center of the Universe."
&
"forget about how we've fucked since we were in trees, THIS is how it's done right."
Oh & yes I said *our genome* earlier,
I am sick too, but I can see again
while you are lost to the delight
of the unbearably bright self-awareness of a naked body.
That fruit was a bit of bite that was more than you could keep down.

7: Not Your Daddy's Prayer

Goodbye Emilia.
            Peace be with you,
            & with my bony lady body,
            & with the Americas.
May Santa Muerte
            bring queerness to our lives
            protect us from ALL illnesses
            & bring balance to our desires
because you want girls & god
& I want wine & girls that don't treat me like a sin.

            Amen.

The cis girl wants to know what your body looks like and doesn't mind the blood on her hands – Mia-Jo Feeley
(she/her)

and mom never thought these were lessons you needed
taught;
how to say no to pretty girls,
how to spot a vulture
how to not take the path of least resistance.

another week, another exhausted fit
another death-bill in the same font as traffic laws
when the violence is mundane,
when the ghosts deluge upon your throat, dead sisters
pound on the walls of your heart
when all you've been is a hunted thing

even you would take anything else
even you would lie   on her table and let her vivisect you
crotch to gullet   like a real
girl

The TSA Took My Penis Away – Mia-Jo Feeley (she/her)

way back from Springfield, the machine swallowed me (kids
always said spitters are quitters)
      Anyway—the TSA took my penis away. They took her
away. My little bomb of
      skin
      Who knows what would happen if we let a whole girl
in the sky! She might not
      come
      down 'till the stars know her bitter taste & even then
she might pull up on the
      event
      horizon of a black hole where she is the event & on the
horizon is a show so
      energetic
      light won't leave.

        Here is where time slows down for the outside
        observer.
        Here is where we never come back.
        Here is her hole.
        Here is your temple.
        Here is the landing strip, the tease, the reveal,
        the baggage claim, the barf bag, the lover at
        the terminal.

the book of aberration – Lindsay Valentin (she/her)

in the atramentous hours scrawled here
as words in a scroll
our futures scribbling forward furiously
as time's hands
we write the book of aberration

pouring down the manila pages
stains yet symbols
to tell the constellations by

and there's only a few windows with lights on
this hour of night
the other denizens of times stygian cavities
smoking out their windows
sipping on flasks of whiskey and examining the sky
like i
don't know what day it is i'll die
so for now i'll just get high
yeah, for now i'll just get high

the wanton want – Lindsay Valentin (she/her)

those last nights we spent at motels
those last days of believing
everything was going to be ok
the ocean's water, sweet as sugar
and the already nostalgic days

I don't know what happened to her
to make her this way
woke up one morning
and found a thief in my bed
creeping like a gypsy
out of my doorway

her waxy skin, so beautiful
against my winter holly sheets
her pinprick eyes closed halfway, always
and that heavy head of blonde hair
her thick thigh meat

we used each other up
like heroin
tossed each other aside
as junkies do

fucked, photographed it, got drunk, got high and laughed all
about it

life is lonely

we filled days with each other, and now

well, she knows

she was consumed by the ether
burned up in the codeine dream
sunk out in the chimera
broke, busted up, and blasted in the head so bad
it's just all vapor to her

and love is but laughter

a joke someone told, useless banter

to serve the wanton want

Waves – Christina D. Rodriguez (she/her)

In the harsh light

    of Brooklyn mirrors,

        I see a year of grief

        outlined in my frame.

Round cheeks of a week

  of tequila and Krispy Kreme.

        The first gray hair

    hidden in a sea of
blackness. Worry lines of
my mother's forehead

        made a transfer to my own.

Hips that love still anchors

    the thought of expansion

        for children take a swing

   at my every step.

I haven't thought much

    of myself these days,

      the moments blur from

        bed to desk to bus seats

along the Outer Drive,

      the lake as expansive

as the days ahead.

In Chicago, I walk

        onto Loyola's campus to go

        to church.

   The rituals don't match,

       the stained glass

        Jesus calls my name,

we can take

        a moment to breathe.
  I walk into the empty

  tomb of all my eternal fears,

  always sitting by

the Mother and the Son.

        I apologize to the idea

                of my father, wondering

                      if I imagined his existence

or if being a skeptic is

          the best form of comfort.

I light a candle

      I never pay for,

        never prepared for,

       never with a dollar in my pocket.

I step out to the campus

        and the God I do believe

in waves.

The lake doesn't mind
if I stand next to it,
quiet and racing.

I can't see where it ends

and I take comfort in

not knowing

the end.

Phases of Being a Daughter – Christina D. Rodriguez
(she/her)

I.

In a two-story apartment above an income tax office, a little girl sits at the window, waiting for him.

Her mother slides a pillow between her small elbows and the windowsill, to soften the imprint beginning to form.

She's already carries the imprint of being second choice to the streets, waiting for the scent of cigars to tuck her in at night, a kiss from a 5 o'clock shadow. She sneaks out of bed when she hears him sneaking back out, the hustle louder than the whispered *stay* against blinds closed for the night.

II.

In a two-story apartment above an income tax office, a pre-teen watches the end of her childhood. Chairs swinging in curses, her mother's eyes beaten shut, he loses years of family beneath his knuckles.

She focuses on the patch of hair on her legs, the signs of growing into his genetics, wondering how many clicks does it take to keep the devil out—the scrap, *click*, scrap, *click* of musical locks as her

mother keeps him from entering days later,
standing vigil against the frame.

III.

In a two-story apartment above an income tax
office, a teenage girl sits in the living room,
waiting for him to leave. Sixteen was
supposed to be sweet, with laughter and
parties, not accompanied visits out of rehab.
He missed her sophomore year of high school,
junior year looking like a repeat offender.

A birthday shouldn't make a difference when you
have a stranger sitting on your couch, eating
cake, watching his every move as if he would
take this occasion to flee into the real world. He
hasn't been real to her in years, a bedtime story
she's outgrown.

IV.

In a dark college parking lot, she waits for his
headlights to stop in front of her. A pit stop
between drive thru and dealing, this isn't a
weekly thing.

She tossed out hierarchy a long time

ago, knowing her place in his ranks.

The ride home is quiet. She'd rather

wait at an empty bus stop, it's more

reliable.

V.

In the form of a spare bedroom in a basement apartment was his redemption.

I need to get away from Mom. She's always on my back. Can I stay with you? I promise I won't be a bother.

Always doing her own thing, she comes in late while he finally arrives into the role of father, years too late to comment on 2 A.M. and *Where you've been?*

He forgot to lead by example.

VI.

In an airport in the Midwest, her aunt says *it's cancer* before she boards, a three-hour flight of a crash inside her head.

He kept falling down and didn't want to worry you.

He didn't want to worry you is a theme of getting on airplanes, sitting in hospitals, paperwork, decisions, paying rent across state lines, reassurance, the statue, the robot, the worry lines, the wheelchair, the losing hair on both heads, the lack of control, the home alerts, his stubbornness, his stubbornness, his stubbornness, the nursing homes, the rehab, the forgotten last birthday, the final flight, the final fight, the loss of awareness, her vigil, his swatting air, her soothing voice, she walks out the room, she needs to breathe, his missed final breath, her knees, his slack jaw, her hoarse voice, arranging the burning, the identification of *he looks like he's sleeping, he's so cold...*

VII.

I've never kissed a corpse before.

Never traced silence along his face.

Never had to walk out a room and know I will never see him again.

Living the final moments of seeing his body as a tug of war,

Torn between running out the room
and never wanting to let him out of
my sight. Torn between touching his
skin and standing in a corner, away
from death. Torn between crying
uncontrollably and telling him *I will
be okay.*
My body demands air as I leave, *don't look back, don't look
back, hand her the papers,* escape...
The parking lot sees the tremble I hide from his siblings.

VIII.

His body is still whole to me.

I've never seen his ashes.

I can't erase his disconnected number from my phone.

I've never been this haunted before.

Do I still have a father?

IX.

Of course, I do.

I'm just a little girl sitting by the window, waiting for her father to come home.

Mad Gowns – Christina D. Rodriguez (she/her)

Your mother is a mad

        wedding gown, defiant

in a pantsuit and high collar blouse,

yet complacent

        in dreams of white

picket fences and strollers.

She goes to City Hall

        with a Brooklyn boy promise,

poses for pictures

        in a sweltering Bushwick kitchen

on an October Indian summer day,

        kissing her heartbreak in the mouth.

Do her cheeks

        become acquainted with

his knuckles before or after the ring?

Does his power

        become a back-handed bullseye

during courtship or after

        the license is signed?

The future is a divided kiss, lined with the only hands she has
known
　　to make her tremble

　　　　　　　in qualm or in exaltation,

　　until one day she birthed passion's broken curse:

　　you, a new witness

　　　　　　　to her desecration,
　　you, the path

　　　　　　　to her salvation,

　　you, the basket

　　　　　　　to place her burdens,

　　you, the vessel

　　　　　　　for all of her fears,

　　you, the one

　　　　　　　she shackles with insecurities,

　　you, the gas light

　　　　　　　she flickers in grief.

　　You try to quell

　　　　　　　the brokenness in men
　　who storm like your father,

　　　　　　　kissing heartbreak in the mouth
　　to distract the curling of their fists.

When you come up for air,

        your mother's reflection stares

back at you, wondering

        if you'll have to fight

her ghosts until you slip on

        your own gown.

Hiding From You at the Hopyard Alehouse – Abbey Lynne Rays (she/her)

The last time I saw you,
I ran
   out the door,
     around the corner,
fear a tangle of thorns
   and lilac prayers.
I did not trust my eyes
    not to sing of heartbreak.
Drunk shadows swelled
   with regret and gathered
 stone-like in my throat
    thundering the sweetness
with its thieving desire.

I still can't say
     if you saw me run.
If it cut your heart
   like a shard of regret
 plunging quickly
the distance of
   past and present.
If that icicle of sorrow
   polluted your Pale Ale,
unraveled your calm and
illuminated your choice
    into the expansion of solitude.
    Or if rather you sat
unaffected
    by the rippling waves of
desire and disgust,
   malleable and pressing,

and still,
   seasons later,
    stealing the air of promise.

Still I Hope – Abbey Lynne Rays (she/her)

I was not naive.
No, I knew
men who kiss your
fingers at night,
tilt your face to
the moon
and beg you to stay,

often wake with
a tangle of haste.
Full of realization
their heart
not ready to leap
farther than bedsides.
Dark mouths a sieve
to last night's song.

A little shatter I
prepare for. I
know desire is
a messy thing.
Still, I choose
hope. Give in to
the frivolous swell
knotting and blooming
beneath my rib
and pray.

The body as a talisman – Kristiana Reed (she/her)

Imagine limbs gilt with gold.

Carefully sewn holes through each wrist,
to loop through rope, to wear flesh
and heart, as a sorely given wish.

The luck of breathing,
eyes blinking in the sunshine.

Imagine—imbued potential;
the magic of winter and summer,
the strength to carry, to cradle,
to love beyond hope.

To lay heavy upon a chest,
your soles left to soak in the soil;
earth your bones have come to know.

I like melancholy, so I write in the past tense – Nabila Abid
(she/her)

My fingers write about how eyes feel so much yet succumb to everything,
The same old routine of rebellion and silent spectators
They say they are my friends, yet I got proof of how badly they speak of me from behind.
How can you expect love when all you do is hate?
My deafening silence speaks volumes of my tolerance with them,
I never believed in wars but, I was always given the battlefield.
I have become organised chaos
Like I always feel,
I like melancholy so I write in the past tense
Yesterday was not mine to keep
Today, Chaos is a friend of mine.

Hijab – Nabila Abid (she/her)

I have always been a symbol of safety and choice unlike the
headlines making a lot of noise,
I am draped around the faces which is a freedom of
expression,
The democracy I have been living in never questioned my
existence before,
Fauzia loves to use me without spreading any lies,
Reimagined resilience,
loving is our jihad.
I am known to be a hijab.
Softening our hearts with a pinch of coexistence,
I wish to be nothing but a medium of empowerment and the
only choice,
I am found missing,
may we return back to our calling.
I am a peace of cloth
While I hope to return to my mammoth.
My only prayer to Almighty is to spread peace.
I belong to you, your sister, and whoever wishes to drape me.
I symbolise protection as opposed to destruction,
Just like the skin on one's body,
I am the jewel for many.
Those who wish to unveil me, do not believe in me.
Radhas wrap me as Odhni, Khadijas wrap me as a veil.
If you don't know then please don't judge me.
I am the symbol of safety.
Solemnly learning to teach thee,
The poison of hate and propaganda
will neither benefit you nor me.
The seed of love and tolerance will together free us.

Cherried Knees – Rachel Jacobs/Phantasma (she/her)

Falling happens
So fast
Before you
Know it
Your palms
Are scraped
And your knees
Are cherries.
The world
Stopped
For just a
Moment.
When I fell
For you
It happened
So fast.
My heart
Became a
Dripping fruit
Squashed
Beneath your
Feet.

The Temple of Athena – Rachel Jacobs/Phantasma (she/her)

In another life
You were Poseidon
And I was Medusa.

You tiptoed so gallantly
Into my home
With a sword like
Contraption.

With a smile
So malevolent,
Even I
Was none the wiser.

As you begged,
As you pleaded,
I gave you your wish.

Laying so still,
Not uttering a sound,
Do not disturb
A busy man.

But I was never
A goddess,
A genie, or witch
To grant you
This wish.

Athena never came
With the crown
Full of snakes.

Instead of the serpents:
I was rewarded with a heavy heart
And the memories that never cease.

BETWEEN THE RIPTIDES – T.C. Anderson (she/her)

a beach ball smacks the surface of the ocean and causes a tsunami on the other side. kids giggle and splash at the bubbles bursting from the shallows.

the sun sizzles the skin of umbrella-coated care-nots as mine puckers under the weight of the deluge. a frisbee flies over the water and i wonder if it's a life preserver that missed me.

my flailing arms kiss the divide between darkness and light briefly. the volleyball players mistake my drowning for surfing.

i hear your whistle pierce the layers, and i have heard the siren before, but it's always been for someone other than me. i see your hands push back against the ocean's pull, and others have fought it before, but it's always been for someone other than me.

you were the only one to see me go under and whisper between the riptides, "are you okay?" when i said i wasn't, you were the only one who helped me claim my breaths from poseidon again.

RESUSCITATE – T.C. Anderson (she/her)

/ *resuscitate* /

The aftershocks of death feel like drowning in the empty, lungs desperate for water to make sense of their pain. When I lost him, the world was made whole again, but the ground beneath still splintered in twain, and I fell helplessly into the darkness–*I'm still falling*–with Shakespeare's soliloquy on my lips. These bards' tales were history, not fiction, as I saw the mortal coil slip through my fingers like sand. I wished not to be, no question mark at its wake, to sleep this weary life away...

/ *compress* /

You were not Romeo, nor I Juliet, but I found tragedy in your eyes, a home familiar to my heart. We knew not what questions to ask but found answers in each other. The violence of the world divided us, and yet our strength rose above its mortalities. We found a hiding place in lost lochs and discovered ourselves 'midst the ashes of history. But the aftershocks returned with the blood on my hands wiped clean with time and misery, and I found the blankness of eternity absent of your soul.

/ *breathe* /

Beyond this death, beyond this grief, we persevere, and we are made one again in this puppet show play. But do you breathe when I cut these strings and go off-script? Do you dream of time's whips and scorns and the undiscovered country as I do? Can these hands that have brought death bring life to you again? Does this fairytale fiction make a coward of my conscience or a victim of life's griefful calamities? *Does my heart beat without your own?*

/ resuscitate /

I now know what questions to ask but have no answers. I only know you are my sadness, my hope, and my love, and it's harder to...*breathe*...without you.

IF IT HAD BEEN ANOTHER ME AND ANOTHER SUMMER – T.C. Anderson (she/her)

your skin pressed against the sun would've been temptation
enough to brave its taunting heat / your eyes would've been
daring enough to upend every metaphor buried
beneath my sands / your lips would've been
reason enough to tease
them with the waves of my
ocean / your hands would've
been drive enough to submerge myself
in star-crossed seas / your tongue
would've been consent enough to

                                  drown,

                                        drown,

                        drown,

                  drown,

              drown.

if it had been
another me and another
summer, your body would've
never graced another shore / but made
home in the depths of my wanting waters / but
this me and this summer only watches you
with longing / hoping the
reverie is enough to
grieve.

PMT – Claire Thom (she/her)

An unsettling energy
rides the tide—
driven by lunacy.
A cloud,
bubbling over
with magnificent rage,
nags the froth forming
on furious crests.
The belly of the ocean
erupts and spews
irritability.
Then collapses, sobbing
into the arms
of the shoreline.

Life Lesson – Claire Thom (she/her)

Old car—
purple like a bruise.
Mum—
waiting
as always.
Me—
head full of homework,
hockey practice
and happiness.
Front seat—
soft
under itchy school skirt.
Ears—
search for radio.

Silence.

Mum holds
my gaze and explains.
My innocence
fades
away.
I´d never sat
next to cancer before.

"Are you going to die?"
is all I can think to say.
Mum´s answer
shatters
my 11 year old world—
"I don´t know, my precious girl."

I remember this
years later,
walking out the hospital.
The nurse was kind.
We laughed
as she squashed
each breast,
right
then
left,
in the peculiar machine,
as if making
a cheese toastie.

"All ok"
I text.
"Excellent news!"
Mum replies.
"I love you."
We write
simultaneously
across the many miles.

Static – Claire Thom (she/her)

on the wireless waves
of nostalgia no telly
vision through milk bottle glasses
of sherry cream
coloured wall
paper on Sunday
crossword clues hard
boiled egg for tea
time still
ticks on Grandfather´s clock
hands light a cigarette end
of the day and night
draws the curtains
hanging onto the memory
loss of a loved one
year ago today

Synthetic Worship – Jessica Berry (she/her)

Sunday best
You excavate your own thighs—carpe vinum!
To seize the wine and hide it (quickly, *quickly*)
Glazed over, worship forward.
Looking to them to see if they look down on you:
A baleful twitch in their smile. Dappled with
That single promise of redemption.
Or did you dream that up?

The synth growls louder.
There's a girl missing.
Nobody knows.
Did you finally land on Jupiter?
Or kneel at the back
Below the cross encased in LED light bulbs

Underneath edicts of a man with his spit in the mic,
Green glitter on those high-court cheekbones.
His excavated thighs of golden pockets:
The end of the rainbow.

All this so he can say:
"Let me pray for you"
Before he has asked your name.

I spend the afternoon imagining our marriage – Jessica Berry
(she/her)

Who would be the first to notice the wasps' coming?
Fecundation in our cavities—
But, quashing their hum.
What a meek, yet masterful, ruse.

How could something living within us go
Utterly unremarked? Vespula *vulgaris*
Wiretapping showers, lining two lips with fur
While we dreamt of the wide-open flutes of tulips.

Eventually, white suits would smoke them out
As all happy endings go…
Sleeked creatures whisked our secrets to their afterlife:
White gold below ground with
Black and yellow
Bones.

Bookology – Jessica Berry (she/her)

When you talk about books...

1.

Your voice is the centre of sourdough bread
Moments ago, resting after an oven's labour.
> Rising out of pages—puncturing the surface of
> water
> Mauve gasps. Thick smile. Wet hair.

2.

We're joined by a rainbow on your bed sheets
Your passionate rabble dials colours' contrast
> Up a notch. Tell me that story again—
> *The Evangelical and The Lesbian?*

3.

And I will swirl notions around my mouth,
Let warm milk coat calves' teeth.
> I'm convinced you know each character
> Like a primary school friend,

4.

Their experiences are locked under your blood.
And I am persuaded to love them—
> To love this knack of picking up a story
> Fast-flickering paper cuts; diving inside,

5.
To pull on the softness of sourdough bread.
Next afternoon, addicted now, I'll need this
        Hypnotic book-chat back. I'll turn to
        Caffeinated strangers and plead for an answer:

What are you reading?

I want Janet Weiss on drums – Carlos Clark (he/him)

I wake up
To the endless loop
Stretch
Cough
Rush of cool hits my feet
And it begins
I want to break it and watch the loop
Grovel and beg at my feet
"Come on you need me"
Maybe
But it's become mundane
Stale and brittle
Time for a new tune
Something loud
Ear shattering
A song of intense joy
I wake up to the endless loop
Is that a snare?
That's new

ALZHEIMERS – Omobola Osamor (she/her)

The walls are closing in.
Faces once-beloved grow dim.
Familiar voices fade into a kaleidoscope of memories.
Echoes from a past, now told by others.
Screens filled with pictures—images picked from a shared
landscape.
Journeyed paths with kinship.
Gatherings of sisterhood and knights, celebrating annual
traditions.
Prints capturing the former, now gathering dust on the
mantlepiece.
Sitting in the corner—observing others.
Hair, once thick black yarned coils, now coarse and grey.
Eyes half shut, barely pierced with light.
Cascaded wrinkles over gnarled digits.
Rainbowed taffeta covering wearied limbs.
Listening to tales I once foretold.
On my knees, I once bounced the teller.
These twin hanging lumps once suckled three.
Is it Monday or Friday? I forget.
Did Christmas come early with gifts for me?
It's Sunday, Grandma—April, not December.
They surround me, singing, this strange banquet of others.
Faces no longer familiar, yet eyes sparkling with
remembrance.
The teller covers me in plush white,
bestowing a linger of a kiss on a weathered cheek.
A tear drops from his eyes onto my nose.
A shutter opens.
A sliver of light shines, illuminating his face.
A second becomes a minute,
In the glimmer, I see him.

My forefinger traces a once-familiar path—I recollect for just a moment.
'Happy birthday, Mama.'
Through the cobweb of memories, I smile.
I cannot remember his name.
But, I cannot forget the love.

SEX – Omobola Osamor (she/her)

Fingers twitching in anticipation.
Limbs taut, bridling with expectation.
Mouth dry in remembrance of feathery kisses.
Nose flared, catching each scent, excitement coursing within.
Hibiscus and rose water juice on clashing tongues.
Leaving trails of fiery embers.
Shall it be as whispered in restroom stalls?
Are your fantasies obliterated or satisfied in rippling tides of
climaxes foretold?
Will her touch be as fervent as his or make her one with you?
Will longing to touch soft mounds be at odds with the
pleasure the phallus brings?
The door creaks open as it swings on its hinges,
Why can you not have a kiss on both cheeks?

CROOKED – Kait Quinn (she/her)

She hangs bone white, scythed
as crescent-cut nail, bow
curved as cunning smirk. Like

she delights in our
small deaths—decayed organs
tossed into turned out graves.

In monthly ache, I
witness her trickery. Lure
cast into ink, she

drags mourning from wild
wood throat. Wax, wane, lick *holy*
from wet heathen lips.

O, to be that bright,
bewitching, pool blood, pull tide,
make magic of night.

Wolves lament, hearts split,
trees scrape stars from sky—tonight
the moon hangs crooked.

JESUS CHRIST, I'M SO BLUE ALL THE TIME *After Phoebe Bridgers* – **Kait Quinn** *(she/her)*

Yesterday tastes like burnt coffee & broken
promises. Mouth of May pools vermillion,
spits iron into moody prose & weeping poetry. He told me,
point blank, about his affair. What an honest man! What a
cruel summer! What a bubblegum peony, sickly honey reality!
Rose-colored glasses slid off my nose
& exposed me: labyrinth of night-shielded secrets, good pain,
violet pain, moon under water—O, I am a constant shade of
blue & the tulips are ruthless & you keep filling my porch with
laughing daffodils to shake the stillness. Sometimes closure is
not the way we want it. Sometimes things just decay,
hydrangea bush unblossoms, & Jesus Christ never had some
holy resurrection.
Sometimes a mood just needs a funeral dirge
& the saddest things glisten like emeralds on concrete.

The Neon Girls – Fiona Dignan (she/her)

this is what I mean to say, when they said
your dress is an owl's stare, try hard
to learn, a hair clip tied like an anchor
to my arch brow, they surround me, three
clammy girls, all yaw yaw and drawl, whatever
is against them smarts to sawdust
the dead rat who couldn't stomach it
the pills, spirals, and Plath book in my desk
marked with scrawls of hearts and XOs
wolf skin shedding at my effort and
paled flesh being licked under sticky
lights manhandled by the boys who thought
a finger a cheeky gift for a sinner, winner black
leather Bibles on Sunday, pasta grease
stuck to the pan on a Monday morning
we trail the streets, sipping the neon street
light spills, easy thrills

I Dream of Foxes – Fiona Dignan (she/her)

Foxes stalk
rife in my imagination
An unexpected visitor on my wedding day
Bushy burnt bright against the winter noon
looking on as I took my vows
I stumbled
on my words tongue swollen caught
as I met the vixen's auburn eye
Come
run, she insinuated
Through skeletal hedgerows and wastelands
Slippered feet bruised and dank
I hesitated
and then committed
She can remain stalking my hinterlands
I am domesticated

I diminish her to a motif
on a cheap mug bought in a dilapidated seaside town
Sips of steamed coffee brace against the caravan's briny
window
A mundane talisman
Mass-produced nature print made ubiquitous
I believed I could reduce her to essence

She returned
Bringing with her the pack of mangy cubs
to feast
My mind's eye jerks on repeat
images of my stillborn daughter ravaged by the pack
Left to the wild to dispose of
No longer challenging, inviting, offering

but reminding me
of what nature can be
Untamed

And how many children do you have? – Fiona Dignan
(she/her)

I answer four, although
what I mean to say is five,
but I don't want to start that conversation
with a well-meaning stranger.
How can I explain that Sasha
is wet ashes dissolved on a Surrey heath?
She has passed through a door
and I can't pick the lock.
She was; tiny blue feet
stained ink black,
footprints on snow white paper,
a pastor's prayer, a minor key.
But I am still her mother.
I still birthed her.
She was still born

Counterfeit Saint – Eddie Brophy (he/him)

Stifled by the platitude wisdoms
and insecure bravados
of a parent made God
you manifest a vicarious mess
weaponizing the trauma
of the next emotional insurrection
can you even fathom
the empathy or emotional fatigue
of putting your aggrandized grief last
for the sake of a tangible tear
I contemplate with melancholy
I gave my soul to a counterfeit heart
I had my children with a surrogate emotion
one day you'll appraise yourself
with no humility to spare
one day the narcissist will have to see
the ones you manipulated
eventually found refuge
in the communal ache of your fallacies
and no longer
will they exist for your affluence of their despair.

September's Lost – Eddie Brophy (he/him)

Wizened by despair,
sequestered by my faults,
July's seduction
now dictates the enormity
of this daunting loss,
my nativity obscured
by the reminder
that mortality
is a bitter lottery,
ravenous and vindictive,
my heart bounced another check,
now I'm emotionally default,
hand me my affirmation,
in a death certificate
or serve me the day before
I last held his hand
I swear,
I'll never make that mistake again,
rueful to a point,
this hurt monopolizes
what's left,
I've pulled the last trigger,
I've swallowed enough
of autumn's bullets
to pacify the hurt I'd normally declare
I lost September to my father's death and your affair.

Odd Uncovering – Georgina Melendez (she/her)

My hands would often smell of unsalted butter and sponge, a mixture that brought the comfort of home to my pale skin. Truth is, it was never easy to get someone to wash the dishes, but I felt awkward to volunteer. The reasoning behind the veil was to be seen without judgment. So, to wet my hands in dirty dish water was my way to put out a bid for love.

1988 rolled by as quick as my red Camaro named Vita. Sweater strands covered the seats and the tears had started early. My car had become the one thing I lived for and the one thing that made me feel like I could do anything. I found the wind against my wavy hair every time I took her out for a drive, without a care to rule my blood.

It didn't take much to drown my sorrow; I knew how and when to break out my disguise. And for a time, I even turned to strong drink. I was the decor flower taped up on the wall during a party. It was my safe place where I could eat yellow cake, and no one and nothing could reach me except my words. I secretly carried a diary and a small pistol long before the laws were passed. My poems had become bullets buried deep inside the tomb of my broken ribs, while the pistol laid suspended upon my belly. It was fully loaded for whoever would try to unearth her. Just try, and she would not flinch.

Be Not Her Strength – Georgina Melendez (she/her)

I could hear the pain(t)stirring in the can—the one that was smeared across that famous grocery store. It's yellow, her favorite color. One that we wouldn't see for a very long time. Aisle four sliced us heavy, and it was the brightest of them of all. The sacred had become disjointed. We couldn't call anyone to clean up the mess, so we turned to the bandaids instead. In my 11 years of small life, I had never seen a wound like this. It was a blue light special with no prize found at the bottom of the cart, only hollow, stolen tins. Emotions in apoplexy, she took away the beautiful yellow color my mother deeply loved. That year the grocery store was shut down and we never heard from her again.

An OK State Motto – Amanda Karch (she/her)
First published in Topical Poetry

A woman wipes her eyes—
allergic to the taste of metallic
blood pooling on tongue from biting
so hard to prevent comments that
leave her feeling less than?
Or mourning the loss of
choice for a body belonging to
one owner, sharing likeness and soul?

Leaving Eden – Amanda Karch (she/her)

I play God with power never asked for,
yet my own tools are weaponized against me.
When they reach for my body
like it was made for their taking,
they remind me at my own altar
where I came from—forgetting
creation embeds itself in my womb,
world's first artist forming bone and
body in an altar, not worshiped
by a man who opens up church doors to
preach my birth from his rib,
stripping me of my own power
at the stake where belief goes to burn,
forgetting a phoenix will always rise
from ashes when her wings are spread
to fly above those who seek shelter
in glass houses and fear getting cut.

She Was Asking For It – Amanda Karch (she/her)

But still you declined, instead
took that innocence, that naïveté
and incinerated it, ashes
flying into her eyes as tears
trickled down her cheeks,

no energy left for the waterfall
you deserved. A beating
of the heart signals life
but her eyes tell a different
story. She was asking for
forgiveness for a crime
she did not commit. She was

asking for red lights and
road closed signs but
all you gave her was a fear
of the dark.

Tale of the Unseen – Liz Yew (she/they)

Because I was born from the rib of my companion,
Because I am not created to be a reflection of him.
Because I do not have a say in naming his creation;
Because I am inferior to him.
Because I am the fool who fell for the trick;
Because I committed the first sin.
Because I am the one who doubted his intentions
Because I am painted a villain in his story.
Because I am not a man who can do no wrong;

Because I am Eve.

But I do not falter and question myself when the
swell of my chest is larger than his,
But I scream and fight to be heard—to bleed and
grow for love and justice.
But I do not bend to his will when his instincts take
control of him;
But I teach my daughters to respect and protect themselves.
But I learn to love myself—for I am no villain

I am no inferior

I am no fool

I am no sinner

I am no man

I am a woman.

IMAGINING ADVICE FROM MY OLD PSYCHIATRIST – Daniel J. Flore III (he/him)

I wish I could talk to my old psychiatrist
not as an official appointment
but just to get together
I imagine myself saying to him,
it feels like my intestines are in a blender—
I have no peace
then I picture him replying,
Dan, what I want you to do
is go out to breakfast with your wife
order the wheat toast
and imagine
a long wheat field swaying in the breeze
and he would write out a real prescription
for me
for wheat toast

HALLUCINATING WHILE MY FRIEND SMOKES POT AND LOOKS AT ME LIKE I'M JESUS – Daniel J. Flore III (he/him)

I see things that aren't there
my friend thinks it's cool
says I'm a poet having visions

but I'm sick and they're hallucinations
so I wish he would shut the hell up about how awesome it is
but he doesn't, he just goes on and on—

"you're like Ginsberg and Yeats...visions man!"
"ya gotta heal the tribe!"
"come on Lizard King, what visions are you seeing?"

I'm sick, you jerk! I say
and I ask him to leave
but I don't get him out
God, it's hard to get a hallucination to go away

We – Michael Brigden (he/him)

We push and we stretch,
reaching out into blue,
we are what we are
what we are is not you,
we have no agenda
no plans and no dreams,
we follow the sun
and gather its beams,
we flow through the air
standing tall or laid flat,
we are all kinds of colours
we are this, we are that,
we thirst for a drink
at times that will change,
we bud and we flower
we are all kinds of strange,
we are what we are
all different in size,
what we do's not for you
you just witness our being
you witness our truth.

Cause and Effect – Michael Brigden (he/him)

If you prick my conscience
with your righteous mind
I may want vengeance
then peace I'll find
within the journey
towards your end,
my once deadly lover,
my immortal friend.

If you show your true self
in your glorious hues
I may take advantage
I may abuse
the power you give me
It is immense
my once deadly lover,
my immortal friend.

THE ODE TO "O" – Effie Spence (she/her)

Oh, jeez, look at the time, 3:38pm and I said I'd do that thing
at four.
On my shelf I put a book about gods,
only, I don't know the real difference between my fault
Or theirs. Or the stars.
Or there's this sense I get that all the corps who told us in
Obsequious fashion stories about my chances, my hopes. *DE
OMNIBUS DUBITATUM!*
"Omnipotence is solely stabilized for
One source," the governments at work
Over sourcing our love of earth to fetch,
Once and for all, a way for us to fall.
Of course, they're wrong.
Objectively, of course.
Oatmeal left burning on the stove,
Opting out of doing things on my
Own.
Owing nothing to helping my woes
Overcoming foes is hopeless, I'm sore, ripping
Offal from bones.
Ogres of whores wearing thin in my mind,
Oiled and ready for the fight of my life.
Older people are none the wiser
Offering words of encouragement,
Obligingly with smiles,
Obtaining a place of self importance.
Occasionally I look up from one quixotic thought,
"Observe me now, like
Ovid wrote of humans becoming trees;
Om namo guru dev namo." The frail
occipital lobe sees what I want, but am I in control?

Orpheus bled a song
On seeing his wife gone
over the underworld
One understood;
Obnoxiously to look back
Obliterates our path. I
Ooze with shame that I didn't get home in time that day
Out of the river styx my
Own paranoia came.
Oared by hordes of unmastered chores,
Open the doors to my heavenly stores!
Oh Omnipotence of my human heart
Occlude these thoughts that I am not
ONE source for myself to get better
Or not.
Orishas, kriyas, nymphs, ghosts, anyone,
Obstruct the drive to destruct myself. I give this
Ode to you to breath, for in this I hope I live,
Ogling at the humor that was my pain.
Oceans and waves become mere tremors,
Oh hey! I feel better, I am a
kitchen witch, full of love
and pepper, Or I am a feral
wife, untethered.

a stretch to me – Effie Spence (she/her)

the waves pacify my dearly held thoughts
that somehow we are tied like knots
each wave laps over my toes
shrinking my nose in that dearly cold
i sing to the sea (well ocean really)
that one day you will belong to me
i wave to you from the coast of California
waiting for news of whether you're gone yet
release the bowing ebbs of flows
of wandering weather and weather woes
asking myself to trust the sea trust
the sun trust in me trust in you that
this will all wash over
and my message will find you on
the shore of Victoria the pacific
holds our hopes in its drops
dearly praying your heart does not stop
over the ocean you fly to me
a stretch of see, merely, a stretch to me
we jump in together, the cold, blue ocean
and waves wash over those worried memories
fast-forward to last summer, swimming in the
Mediterranean.

THREE SISTERS – Effie Spence (she/her)

PART 1; THE FIRST BORN

In a puddle, of deep sea green, there swims
a thing that resembles me.
She dances around in obstructing circles
to mock or instruct me into joining.

PART 2; THE SECOND BORN

The sky scrapers and roaches breathe life into my
gait, darting around the cement scape. In a pool,
of blueish grey, I taste a life of New England trees
and my little muse circling me
to judge me or coax me into laughter.

PART 3; THE THIRD BORN

Dancing between palms and plays,
acting like the ocean doesn't scare me.
In a pool, golden green, I taste the stars
and hope they find themselves in me.

Mirror Image – Ryan Kenny (he/him)

He stares at me, eye to eye,
I notice that his eyes are as blue as the ocean or a cloudless
sky,
But within the blue, there is no semblance of a soul,
Who is he? Why is he here? Why will he not speak? I already
think he's an asshole.
Our eye contact does not falter or break,
And he retraces every single move I make,
He's mocking me now, this is getting weird,
As do I, so he too scratches his beard,
What a prick!
Standing before me, clearly taking the piss,
But I cannot look away,
He has fixed me on the spot and stirred within me a sense of
dismay,
An anger is now rising inside me, starting to burn like hate,
I ball my hand into a fist and hope it's not too late,
I must fight him, I can see it now, it's so much clearer,
I take my fist and throw it forwards as a punch and - SMASH -
it was a mirror!
Sorry, it seems I'd zoned out a bit there,
Distracted by my self-abusive mind that trapped me with a
stare,
I'd fallen down a rabbit hole of self-rejection,
And had a wordless argument with my own reflection,
But as I stand here now, my hand covered in blood,
I realise I must use this power of introspection for good,
So when I look in the mirror now, what is reflected back at me,
Is a man who tries to see himself in a light of positivity.

The Garden, After Rachel Long – Rebecca Green (she/her)

Dinner was bread
followed by blankness.
Years later, the chair he fell from
is still on its side.

If the cavity grows wider
you're going to have to kill yourself.
'John, I'm late.' Or: *'you shit,*
why did you ever leave me here?'

Silence. The crossword. Watch
the cricket in the summer.
Hear the doctor listening to your heart.
Hear him hear nothing at all.

You can't give your family
news like this
and not clear out the cupboards
before they have to.

Fall off the same chair or
go to the hospital. Take off your slippers
though no one knows where they'll go.
Hold a silver basin, in your hands.

Beg forgiveness for the thing you want to do
Say the prayer to rid you of guilt.
Say it in the tongue your dead husband taught you.
Where will we meet, this time around?

—Will you slow the dam,
like a tree crammed in the mouth,
or will a deluge of water
carry me to the afterlife?

Reflections – Rebecca Green (she/her)

The light shines brighter from her forehead, than it does from my own.
She who grasps the sleeping dog and shakes it to wake in a moment

I just watch blood run in slow rivers from the soles of my feet, the glass I stomped on withering to sand, the blood running out to sea.

If God is a whisper, His wife is a howl.
I displaced my plants in the hopes of a better life, for room for them to cast around and lean into brighter days. But it grew grey a day later and their waving hands withdrew.

Her back is an arch and a dip. I imagine rolling a marble down her spine, watching it spin before it lands in a heavy crescendo; enough to make the heads turn in ten local houses.

I am on the edge. The fingers withdrawing after beginning the journey; the tremor of an arm lifting a child for too long, of refusing to let go.
I am a broken thing and She is the howling wife.

Cake – Rebecca Green (she/her)

My mother was told
that a baby
was barely possible.
Washed her hands of it
took out the mixing bowl

and,
dash in the rum,
dash in the raisins,
soak a batter with ginger
brought me to life.

I emerged from treacle
dripping
down the family chin.
Make sweet the baby,
lay thick and heavy
from the nail
to the elbow.
All of us be fistfuls
of potential miracles
and we not be washed away.

Nothing, Killing *After Emily Skaja* – Shilo Niziolek (she/her)

I wake into the stabbing of a premenstrual migraine.

And more than that, I can't stop crying at every beautiful thing.

Smoke twists off my joint, into the air around me

and I close my eyes to the woman in illness that I have become.

Three times this year I've reapered, reaped, been reaped.

Hands gloved, I ushered a pine sisken, feathers bristled into a cardboard box.

Frantic after hours of trying to eat and discovering it couldn't swallow.

Emily Skaja writes:

"why is there nothing wild in you

to explain it, nothing killing;"

I place my hand over the lid of the closed box as I speed to the Audobon

as the bird, in between long intervals of silence where I fear it has died,

flaps its wings violently and lets out a dying chirp.

They have already told me it will die.

It dies, not with my hand placed on the box.

In sleep, I dream of being fucked by someone I once knew,

and I wake to an orgasm, my body untouched; my partner in bed beside me.

Why is everything wild in me unholy,

to explain it, for hours I marvel at the weight of:

ice rain pummels tree branches and shatters them on the ground.

I race into the snow in green wool socks to the sound of screeching,

My dog has a squirrel by the tail, protruding from the small black box

that it made refuge of, and I make him drop it.

I place gloves on my hands and carry the box to the side yard.

"it's okay, it's okay, it's okay"

A large eye stares at me, squeaking, through the see-through lid.

One after the other, I pry the edges open with a long flathead.

I watch as the last edge pops and the creature scampers away, hollering.

There was a time I lay down in the cab of my white ford pickup. A handful of antidepressants;

when the boy I loved found me, he stuck his finger down my throat until I retched.

"why / am I the chased thing horrified

to overtake myself,"

Emily Skaja writes.

In December I have high-grade cell lesions

scraped from my cervix with a hot metal wire

and when I wake, I ask the nurses for my partner, but I do not recall it.

I once tried to slice open my wrists with dull sea glass under a bridge.

Why am I the haunted thing, horrified

Watching myself chase myself.

I try not to recall the paralyzed squirrel across the fence

Before the neighbor came down on it with a shovel for a merciful death.

"it's okay, it's okay, it's okay"

Bright yellow daffodils stare at me across the yard.

In middle school I walked into the garage to a deer hanging by its feet,

Stomach sliced down the middle, a cavity of pink.

For months I do not sleep.

Why is everything wild in me

killing.

So You Wanna Talk About How I'm The Dead Girl In The Painting – Shilo Niziolek (she/her)

1.

I'm not saying I'm Ophelia floating in the water before she
drowns,

but lately when I try to fall asleep, I can't catch my breath, like

Hamlet's hands are holding me underwater, my legs tangled in

ragweed, seaweed, there's lost souls under the River Styx and
they

think I'm ready to join them. I won't go under into the dreamy
place

where flowers will float me on down the stream, and it isn't
until I

swallow a tablet of Ativan that I'm the river and the sky and
Ophelia

singing before she died. They say: forgive him, he knows not
what he

does, but I've got forgiveness for no man, no jesus up in the
clouds,

only the heron that sits on the riverbank, watching me drown,
her

keen yellow eye silent, unjudging, waiting to deliver me.

2.

When I was a child, a young girl my age a town over was

found chopped up and left in a dumpster, her scooter intact

beside her. Before that I climbed on top of the dumpster in
our

neighborhood so I could see over the rim of the trailer park to

a field where horses roamed. After that, I became afraid of

dumpsters and what lurked inside them, learned that people

out there thought girl's bodies were yesterday's trash. When

grown men drove by my 12-year-olds body, craned their
necks,

honked their horns, I flipped them off. Fuck if I'm going to

become another casualty of my female body, I thought, as if a

mere finger could stave off their gnawing hunger. But then I
fell

in love with a boy who became obsessed with extinguishing
my

light. It burnt brighter than his own, his already yesterday's cig

ashes blown away in the wind. And when I hid from him on a

rainy night in a ditch, pocketknife curled into my cold hand, I

became the girl in the dumpster and realized I had been her all
along.

3.

There's a market for dead girls. It's bigger and wider
than you could even fathom. When you Google dead
girl paintings there are hundreds of listings. Under Fine
Art America it says, "Choose your favorite dead girl
paintings from 695 available designs." I don't want to
be your favorite dead girl. I don't want my head stuffed
and mounted on your wall, glassy eyeballs following your
every move across your room. I won't go walking after
dark and if I do, I'm taking my 75-pound pit bull. He's kind
and scared of everyone, especially men, but you don't need
to know that; you just need to imagine his jaw the size of
your face closing around it. And when you hear his bellow
it's my rally cries you're hearing, for all the dead girl paintings
plastered on the museum walls. We are a veritable field of
wildflowers, on our backs, singing and floating down
a stream, our bodies brush strokes before we're dead.

We All Got Burnt *After Olivia Gatwood* **– Shilo Niziolek**
(she/her)

I can only write poetry if I read poetry.

I need someone else's words to enter me first.

It's in the overlay.

Like when Olivia Gatwood writes:

"i did not lose someone i love. i lost someone i once loved."

What it means is I can curl my body

up around the words and weave into them.

I can park a dead boy down,

right there on the poem.

Because I've got dead boys too.

One

Two

My dead boys are just like your dead boys.

One I didn't love but thought about it,

a time or two.

The other, well, I loved with childlike wonder.

In middle school at the skatepark

He tried to kiss me on the lips.

I turned my face and gave him the cheek.

I've got dead boys that aren't dead boys too.

Three

Four

The one that gripped my breasts while we kissed,

Like doorknobs, like fistfuls of grass,

Something he wanted to pull out.

Leaving putrid yellow bruises that

Battered my pale skin for weeks.

The one that had half a front tooth

Knocked clean out, then got drunk,

then kissed me on the floor of my friend's room.

He wanted to love me but, girl, I would never.

Five

Six

The one that kissed me

when he wanted to kiss another.

The one I kissed

when I wanted to kiss another.

Seven

Seventy

Seven Hundred and Seventy-Seven.

The one I loved. The one I loved. The one I loved.

He's the deadest of them all.

Gatwood writes:

"I want to know

what it means to survive

something.

/

does it just mean

I get to keep my body?"

The one that said, "Where did you learn those moves?"

The one that cut my labia with a jagged nail,

then punched and spidered my windshield

with his fist, cause I could no longer fuck.

The one that knew how to kiss, so as to buckle my knees.

The one that said, "No matter where you go, I'll find you."

The one that held his hand over my mouth.

The one that I hid from in a ditch with a pocket-knife

while he drove up and down the black and rainy logging roads

and called my name and screamed my name and cried it.

The one who wept, "I'm sorry, I'm sorry, I'm sorry."

The one who left fingerprints on my skin.

Eight

Nine

Ten

Eleven

The one who stole me from my abusive lover

(thought he was saving me)

Who wanted to be choked, be hit.

And I cried while we kissed,

closed my eyes to the face that wasn't his.

The one I didn't love

who tilted my chin up gently.

The one I didn't love

who loved another.

The one I was with just to feel.

The one who loved me

when I loved another.

The one who loved me when I loved another.

The one who loved me when I loved another.

Ring around the rosie,

A pocket full of dead boys.

Ashes, ashes.

"On your knees," they said.

Down, down, go down.

Women – Bharti Bansal (she/her)

I live under the shadows of my birth givers

Shadow formed by my mother's infinite sacrifices and my father's intolerance for his own emotions

He believes that men should never curl themselves into a tiny speck of a dot, lay on bed and cry on their lover's chest

Yet every single day I see him negotiating with the beliefs that are not his own

But given to him as souvenirs from his father who fell in love twice, under the same house where his two beloved lived, as women should, without a voice, and stifled anger boiling like a hot spring in a cold valley.

I dare not challenge my father's silence

For everything which is not a rebellion, is a fight without victory

Maa has told me time and again how women should suppress their discontent as heavy sighs and sleepless nights

This is not to say my father is a bad man

(I cannot write without feeling the weight of his love, you see guilt sometimes is an apology)

My father has shaped me into a woman who carries her silence with her, and firmly seeks to be heard without saying a word.

In our home, what's not said lingers in the air like the ghost of a child dying in a war, who believes God grants his every wish, so he stands in front of the gun and takes the bullet in the hope of being rewarded for being a good kid

In our world, we don't accept apologies for the mistakes of our parents, but simply forget who we are.

Forgetfulness saves, especially when one is drowning, and we are the kids of adults who couldn't row the boats to the shore, so they told us how water's was the only surface that held bodies.

I am writhing with this foreboding sorrow

Asking my mother if time really heals wounds or does one become complacent?

I have seen my grandmother shaping her seven daughters into women who should and must know that men hide their hearts, either in noisy anger or sullen silence

So they must listen to the words that lie at the tip of their tongues.

My mother has spent years trying to hear what my father didn't have the courage to say

My aunts have walked the same path, standing under the same tree which bears the same fruit they have tasted over and over again.

And now when I have grown into an adult, I know that love doesn't compensate for the space left behind by the absent conversations.

Our house is an alias for conformity

I wake up to the same old beats of my heart trying to make sense of this need to be free

From the wounds my parents passed on unknowingly,

I am trying to forgive my mind for forgetting that my body isn't just a space where goodness of character blooms,

That womanhood doesn't not mean blind acceptance

That even though I have seen women of my life trying and trying,

I should remember how sometimes too much forgiveness isn't love

But a reflex, of generations of women doing the same,

Because they weren't told anything better than this.

I forgive my father for not knowing the difference between hurt and anger, or how love can become a savior only if one dares to look beyond the confined windows of truth they were taught by their fathers and grandfathers.

I forgive myself for believing that sacrifice is the only love language, or strength is just a woman carrying grief like a fetus, nurturing it as it becomes parasitic,

I forgive myself for not knowing that my grandmother didn't deserve all of this hurt, for her patience wasn't sheer acceptance but a scream that I still hear the echoes of

Language – Bharti Bansal (she/her)

I often fail badly at language

Conversing has always been my biggest flaw

So when my cousin compared my face to a dead body, I answered back with silence

The colours of my brown skin aren't the shades you find in rainbows

But only in the drought-stricken countries

And crematoriums with piles of wood stashed in the corner

I, then, started applying a red lipshade,

And haven't stopped since.

Maa sometimes says it's too bright for my age

How do I tell her that I answer back only after years have passed

That my silence communicates only after damage has been done

That I still believe my body is a dead house which I feared the most when I visited my nani,

How much anger is hatred?

How much love is sympathy?

I haven't asked questions ever since I fell on the escalator of a shopping mall too big for a girl from a village nobody knew about,

It wasn't funny to me as I spent days searching how to step on it without holding somebody's hand

I must have known that people who hold you are sometimes the same as those who laugh the loudest on your fall.

Language is comforting only when it's a smile

But oftentimes, it's a sneer for those who aren't fluent in it.

It has its own charm, I believe

But nobody believes you with bad grammar

Or incorrect punctuations, you see, inadequate capitals in the middle of the sentences are taken for screaming

And starting every line with "because" becomes redundant,

So, lately I have been reading all the poems with perfectly crafted sentences

And I find how we have the same voice, same need to see the butterflies from the lens of a flower, same desire to write into words, the laughter of our grandmothers, or talk about the difference between hurt and heart

Yet somehow the language of grief is different from the rules of English

I am a refugee sitting on the borders of words which are too obscure,

Metaphors which are too lazy to be seismic

You see, someone who learns a new language never forgets the taste of those first mispronounced word on their tongue.

I remember the first English song I ever composed with my sister was made of incoherent words because I believed anything which was far from the grasp of understanding made it "foreign"

I am yet to learn how to write small effective sentences, with phrases without passive voice

But I am convinced that I was wronged, and there is no other way to write it

I am an immigrant taking shelter in a language which promises me home

Yet after all these years, when it rains I am reminded of how घर sounds, how it flows from my vocal chords onto my lips, and stays there until someone calls me back into the four walled room, and talks about how warmth is a privilege for those who have known cold intimately

From a distance at which death stands.

Language is as much an ocean as a barrier,

It allows people to reach the other side as much as it drowns

I have seen grief from the eyes of a half-learnt parlance

And it doesn't get easier, saying it hurts without seeing people squint their eyes as they try to understand how my lips move,

It doesn't get better when one decides to notice the difference between खूबसूरत and beautiful, how "ugly" is a small word which doesn't take much out of the speaker, but the receiver, always the receiver

How when the same cousin constantly looked down upon me, with the kind of hate that develops gradually over time, like a poisonous cup of wine, I tried remembering what word best described it,

What word was heavy enough to drown the hurt she caused,

What sentence was compact enough to tell that I didn't deserve this translation of anger,

I could never find one.

Language has, at times, betrayed me,

Told me different stories about people who rebel by hating,

Asked me to forgive them, forgive her

There is no word in English that talks of sweet revenge and justifies it,

There is no room for a sentence starting as a prayer and turning sadistic by the end of it

"I wish she finds in the world, the same hurt she gave me"

There are so many flowers and so little bees,

Too much forgiveness, so little forgetting

So, time and again when the world collapses into a mere blot of ink on an old man's secret journal

I remind myself that there is always a symbiosis between a native speaker and their dialect,

It helps its speaker to find space for poetic justice,

Unreserved for an orphan of words, who navigates through the world, crying like an infant whose stomach hurts, which his mother always mistakes for hunger.

FICTION

Mr. Cameron – Amelia Jacob (she/her)

You told me once your grandmother was a glamorous woman, who other women labelled wild, who answered to no-one. With her inky tresses and painted doe eyes, she was an enigmatic siren, familial deserter. When your father wanted to hurt you, he spat at you: *you could be twins, darling.*

You try to remember her sometimes, but your mind fails you. It conjures up vague images of matted, black hair threaded with long strands of silver, her pinched mouth slathered with dry, peach lipstick several shades too light for her dark complexion. You recall a figure hunched away in the murmuring dark, a groaning hospital bed superimposed like a child's collage onto mahogany cabinets groaning with ancient china. It wasn't the sort of life which suited her.

When we were seventeen, your father showed me an old photo of your grandmother. It was a Friday evening in December and I had arrived at your house ten minutes before the time you suggested, watching my breath melt into thin, hot clouds as I hopped from foot to foot on the front step, until the blue glare of my phone announced it was exactly half past the hour.

I regretted my punctuality almost immediately after I knocked gingerly on the door, hearing the frantic steps of your mother approaching. She welcomed me in her girlish way, stretching the greeting out on her tongue like toffee, before ushering me into the small lounge where your father sat. He was washed yellow by the lamp curved around his drooping head, and I was reminded of the way sunflowers slump when dusk falls. "She'll be down soon," your mother said, before scuttling out of the room. The earthy, thick scent of her perfume coiled around us after she left, and I coughed discreetly.

As I stood uneasily by the door, your father sat in silence and stared at me levelly. Minutes seemed to pass by, and I could feel myself sweating through my top. I realised your face was almost identically mirrored in the fading outline of his chin and brow, like you'd sprung from his head fully formed.

A pile of papers sat on his lap, and when he shifted uncomfortably in his seat several danced to the floor. He made a move to bend and pick them up, forgetting himself, before hissing through gritted teeth and retreating. His body stiffened, and his eyes remained fixed on his lap. Stepping forward lightly, I scooped the papers up and deposited them onto the arm of his chair. I was careful not to touch him, but before I could withdraw my hand, your father grabbed my wrist just hard enough for me to feel a low ache bloom under the pressure of his fingers.

"Would you like to see a photograph?" he asked me quietly. "Y—yes," I stuttered. His tone didn't sound like he cared about the answer.

The photograph in question was worn and yellowed with age: there was a dark skinned woman in the centre, primly dressed in a crisp nurse's uniform. Her haughty stare was set in sepia, above full lips that turned down jaggedly at the edges. A cursive note on the back stated in smudged black ink: *March 1956, pregnant with Stephen.* Near the worn corners of the paper small watery marks were liberally splattered around the cursive script.

"I tell Hannah all the time that my mother was lovely when she was young," your father said wistfully. "I'm not entirely sure she believes me." He laughed conspiratorially, a short, exhaled wheeze, then trailed off awkwardly.

Silence resumed. The floor upstairs creaked above our heads, and I heard a faint laugh travel through the boards. *Please come down,* I willed you. It crossed my mind briefly that this was the most Mr. Cameron had ever said to me. I had only known you for a matter of months at this point, and during this time alone, your father had deteriorated rapidly, older and frailer with each visit I made to your house. His black hair was now streaked with washed out grey, and the lines on his face wrought his jaundiced complexion into deep wells.

He shot me a satisfied smile as I squinted at the photo, was tightly clutched in his fingers. He gently brushed his shaky thumb over your grandmother's chignon. The minutes seemed to crawl by, until eventually he replaced the photograph in its slot in the album nestled on his lap and sighed quietly. I could distantly hear your mother chopping vegetables, and shifted uncomfortably in my seat. *Please come down.*

Next to your father's chair, there was a wall covered in family photographs. I could see, amongst various baby photos and birthday shots, an image of a far younger version of your father by a waterfall, standing tall with the confidence that only attractive men who know they are desired possess. Young Mr. Cameron held a beer bottle carelessly in his right hand as he smirked at the photographer, his eyeline reaching up and past the lens. He was shirtless, wearing loose shorts, his bare feet curled into the ground. It struck me as an odd photo to have displayed publicly. There was an arrogant sexuality to him that I was embarrassed to have witnessed. I looked back down to the man sitting in front of me and thought the younger version of your father would have broken him to pieces with a careless slap to the back.

As if my thoughts were advertised across my face, your father turned around to follow my gaze. When he caught me looking at the framed picture behind him, he wheezed again. He seemed almost smug that I'd noticed it.

"I tell Hannah *I* was lovely when I was young too," he said, his gaze bright. I could see beads of sweat flickering on his forehead. Your thumping steps emanated from the floor above like a death knell, cutting through the heavy air. I stared at a bulging vase of dried flowers that was placed on a table in the centre of the room, covered by a thin blanket of greyish dust. The heat of the room was giving me a headache, and when your father's right hand landed heavily on my thigh it felt feverish, lurid. His hand slid under my skirt and up, so slowly, until it was shaking, moving in between my legs. The room seemed to blur in shades of yellow. I thought of potatoes swimming in fat. I thought of the colour of bile and pollen scraped under my chin. I stared in disbelief at your father, frozen, as one wrinkled petal dropped from the vase and danced to the floor, as he groaned and finally snatched his hand away from me, shaking it ruefully.

I stood up, stunned. I closed the door slowly as I left, not looking back, careful not to creak the hinges. An odd lump had caught in my throat and I massaged it away. *I'm sorry–family emergency.* I texted you as I left the house, apologising, thanking your mother for welcoming me. I felt the weight of her bemused gaze following me as I shut the door.

I went home and cried. I bit my nails off until the quick glistened like animal fat and avoided your messages. The shame settled on my chest like mould and unfurled itself, spreading across my lungs. I breathed in and felt the shroud of it fall across my chest. You didn't understand my distance, but you weren't the sort of person to chase. I was your newest friend, and most expendable.

The next week, the temperature dropped. The trees seemed to shrug off their leaves overnight, leaving a brown mulchy residue all over the pavements that got clumped into the soles of my shoes. I would run every evening at twilight and watch the sun sink further behind the greying clouds with every pounding step. Fragile sheets of ice embroidered the ground, glistening wetly in the morning sun, and on one Friday evening, at almost exactly the same time I had arrived at your house several months previously, I received the news that your father had died.

When you called me later in the week, you were wailing with the abandon of a child. The hospital had assured you that he died instantly. Aneurysms are elusive and hard to understand. You told me you'd never forgive yourself for not telling him how much you loved him, how much you would miss him. You told me there was no one as strong as him, no-one as respected, as dignified. I sat on my bed and listened, my head resting against the cold wall. The mould spread from my lungs into my stomach, curling its way around my intestines, but I kept quiet. The chance of confession floated away like a pipe dream.

On the day of the funeral, I arrived at the church late, blaming the traffic, avoiding eye contact. I hugged your shuddering body tightly and said *I'm sorry, I'm so sorry*. You smiled at me blearily and thanked me for my support. Your mother, clumpy mascara rubbed under her eyes, patted my arm lightly and said nothing. You and I stepped through the doors of the church arm in arm, before I released you to walk ahead of me, down the aisle to the coffin, which your mother had covered in enormous, white lilies.

I stepped forward hesitantly. The lilies looked obscene, like swollen flesh. The coffin was closed, thankfully, with only the same photo I had noted on your living room wall framed in gold and placed on the top. I knew I should move forward, but my legs were made of iron, and I couldn't will them to move.

Straight ahead, I saw you thanking another mourner, folding your tall frame down in order to embrace her.

When it was your turn to speak during the service, I could tell you were on the brink of tears again, your mouth contorted at the edges. You exhaled lightly, gazing up at the crowd. The wooden arches of the church rose behind you, the stained glass washing your skin into circular patterns. You raised a jewel-coloured hand to your hair and brushed it behind your ear as you opened your mouth.

My father was a complicated man, as I'm sure many of you know. Despite this, I've never met a man who loved his wife more, or who raised his children with the same respect and pride. I will miss him more than I can ever say, or fully understand myself. On behalf of our family, thank you so much for attending today. I know he would be proud of his legacy.

You sat down in the front row as the minister thanked you for your words. I felt a heavy tear drop onto my chin and dabbed it away with the corner of my scarf. I stood up and walked quietly out of the church. I didn't look back.

The Lady and the Octopus. – Alice Whiting (she/her)

It was a Sunday and I decided to visit the aquarium. The dulcet sound of gurgling water paired with the low hum of artificial lighting painted a pleasantly comforting scene that I did not find dissimilar to the atmosphere of an average chain restaurant filled with fake plants and themed table settings. Yet the surrounding glass tanks gave the illusion of large black windows and revealed glowing shapes of fish that swam past like small spaceships, making me feel that I was in a different city or a different world entirely.

In the entrance I stopped to look into a large, glass column lit up by neon light. Through the darkness I stared at small, transparent mushroom shaped creatures that had no brains but looked like ultraviolet angels. They drifted in lazy chorus, waltzing slowly within the circles of a superficial current that would only cease when the janitor hit the lights.

I wore a leopard print dress.

I returned to leopard print frequently; tight, figure hugging, perfect for meeting strangers within the perimeters of the asphalt jungle.

As I walked through the long corridor gazing into the tanks, I had the notion that I was window shopping. Here a puffer fish, there a rock lobster. I walked past them all, stopping briefly to watch the sharks dart from one end of their aquarium to the next. Despite being locked up they retained their hunting energy.

I stopped at the shark tank to apply my lipstick and the predators circled slowly, hungry for flesh.

The octopus lay at the bottom of a large tank, where on a lower level, you could see him up close. He looked depressed. His tentacles lay around him limply, and I felt in my heart a deep pang of sadness for the creature.

His thick skin looked as if it was made of plastic or rubber, like a toy dinosaur. I longed to reach in and run my hand down his sad body, to feel for myself, the bumps of burgundy skin, the rippled white under belly, his kiss shaped suckers.

The sign next to his tank read:

"From the Antarctic Ocean. Love a bit of existential dread, partial to loneliness, long swims, moonlight."

It was loneliness that brought me to the aquarium. The same loneliness that made me sit up sending messages to strangers at night and searching for meaning within a brief exchange or unexpected phone call from the past.

I descended the spiral staircase to pay him a visit, the smell of salt water fresh on my tongue mixed with a kind of fatigue that radiated from the large aquarium where the octopus lived. As I approached the tank the octopus turned his gaze to me, the single eye that faced me was so human looking that I gasped out loud and extended my fingers to the glass between us. He moved slightly and we stayed for a moment, staring.

Without a second thought I had climbed back up the spiral staircase and navigated my way through an arrangement of plastic foliage in order to reach the entrance to his enclosure. My legs hung over the edge of the tank and the octopus swam up towards me. Two of his arms wrapped around my legs and pulled them apart while two cradled my head, one arm lifted my dress, another tentacle slid into my open mouth and wrapped around my tongue. The octopus began to kiss my neck, the sound of the water and the slap of the small waves moved me quickly.

He pulled me into the water and undressed me completely.

A small crowd of zoo keepers had gathered and were starting to watch, holding their buckets of fish heads, but the octopus released his ink so we were hidden. Then he loved me in the black wet darkness where I could no longer see my legs or his tentacles, only his bright blue eyes, more human than ever.

What Will It Take – Asher Phoenix (she/her)

She sat on the ledge of the wall, soaking up the summer night. She was fiddling with her lighter. Watching the flame dance from the breeze. A cute, happy couple strolled by holding hands, as she slipped the lighter into the back pocket of her jeans.

She got up, pulled her hood up over her head, and started walking. Exhaling the smoke into the dark of night, she looked ahead at the trees swaying in the wind. The cars honked, and she listened to the chatters of nightlife.

Her phone tickled her thigh as it vibrated. Taking it out of her pocket, she sighed as she read the message. She grabbed the joint that she had behind her ear, and sparked it up. It took her three tries to light it because of the wind. The third time as she flicked her lighter the flame burnt her thumb. She dropped the lighter, swearing. She picked it up and flicked it to make sure it still worked. As she struck it down, a weird orange-ish glow formed around her, and then it made a large *boom*. She looked around to see if anyone got hurt or even heard the noise.

She started walking as she finished her joint. Hearing footsteps, she stopped to look behind her. As she turned around, she took several staggering steps back.

"What the fuck..." she said, catching her balance.

She took a small inhale and looked around as she exhaled. A little girl stood in front of her. First she blamed the joint, thinking maybe it was fucked with or something. Both her, and the little one looked each other up and down.

"You're high as hell, but it's not the Mary Jane. I guarantee that," said the little girl.

"Is this some kinda prank or something?" she asked, poking the girl.

The little girl smiled, "Nope, not at all."

"Then explain this to me." she said, kneeling in front of the girl.

"I'm you. Well, the younger, cuter version of you!" pointed the little girl.

"How's that possible?" she asked, thoughtfully. "That shit only happens in movies."

The girl became serious, "I'm here to help you. Well, us."

"Help us?" she said, frowning.

"Yes, we both have a problem that we need to solve," explained the little girl. Confused, she began to help the younger version of herself over to the curb. "I don't need your help for that," sighed the girl, limping.

"Sorry," she mumbled, as she walked with the little girl.

Both versions moved the same way, with the exception that one was faster than the other. The little girl explained what the problem was, but her older self didn't know how to fix it. She knew that the problem had been unresolved for many years.

As a girl, she had always tried to prove herself to certain people, and no matter what she did, or how hard she tried, it was never good enough. The little girl worked hard in school, but even trying her hardest, sometimes she would slip up. She had an attitude like a pistol, but she eventually came around. She did the best she could, and maybe one day she would get the approval she was searching for.

Battling sadness and anger, the little girl struggled as she grew older. She hid secrets, because what she struggled with was her sexuality. Even though she was drowning and lashing out, she still tried her best. Still, for some people, she was never good enough. She grew angry inside though, the majority of the time she had a smile on her face, and knew exactly how to make others laugh. She tried and tried to ignore the negative whispers in her mind, but they kept getting louder and louder.

They both laid in the grass, blurting out solutions, making silly jokes that only the two understood, all the while laughing at themselves and each other. After a moment of silence, the older girl spoke, "look...we're never going to get the approval from them or whatever." She was angry. Nothing would change the past.

"I know. Look, I'm only 8. I don't know all the answers, but can't we think of something else?" the younger girl plead. The older girl, nodded, clicking her lighter as she thought. The girl tapped the older version on the shoulder, "I think I got the answer! Nope false alarm."

"I got nothing kid," she shook her head and looked at the little girl. She might be older now, but she was still unsure. She felt like she was letting her younger self down, all over again.

"I got it!" cried the little girl, cheerfully.

"What is it?" she asked

"Maybe we could find a fortune teller?"

"Seriously?" she laughed with a smirk

"Hey, I'm only 8 remember," said the little girl, shrugging her shoulders.

"Not a bad idea, but I'm not wasting my money on that" she answered, patting the little girl's back.

Suddenly, a question came to her, "wait...can you see into the future?"

"Only up to a certain point, not exactly into the future" explained the little girl.

The two hung out for a while just talking and laughing. It started getting chilly, so the older version handed the younger version her hoody.

"Well, I enjoyed this chat, but I gotta get going," the little girl said while getting up.

"How does this work?" she asked.

"Let's see, I go to sleep, then I get up and get ready for school," the little girl started sarcastically.

"Damn, you're sassy as hell!" she said with a smirk.

"Here, gimme your lighter," said the younger girl, extending her hand out.

"No! 8 year olds can't play with lighters," she stated, taking a step back.

"Damn, at least I tried," shrugged the little girl.

The two of them stood in the middle of the street. The older version flicked open the lighter, sparking the flame three times.

"Kid!" she yelled.

"Yeah?" called the little girl.

"I'm proud of you!" she said, with a big smile.

"Right back at you!" said the little girl with a huge smile. She started to walk away, but turned at the last minute. "Listen, let the ink bleed!"

"What does that mean?"

"You'll know…" the little girl smiled, again. "Trust me, you'll see when it's time; you'll cherish it for a lifetime."

She nodded, adding, "One last thing."

"Yeah?" asked the little girl.

"You got fucking spunk!" said the older version, mirroring the young one's smile.

The older girl flicked the lighter a fourth time, and an orange-ish glow formed around the little girl, just like it had around her at the beginning of the night. The little girl waved and smiled her contagious smile, then vanished. She shoved the lighter into her pocket, pulled her hood over her head, and headed back home.

Jane gets a promotion – Kristiana Reed (she/her)

She had been rehearsing in the mirror for months. They didn't think she had it in her. The patience. The guile. The ability to plan ahead and execute each stage perfectly.

She was wearing a tailored suit. She figured it best to look the part; she wanted to impress, after all, this was her only chance to prove herself. The years were coming on fast, those for pleasure were gone, the future was about action and building the life she had always deserved.

*

Dick waited by the gates for Nell. She always took her time, but Dick never worried as the moment he began to entertain a daylight kidnapping, Nell would emerge from the school building. Today she was arm in arm with a smiling blonde, their faces animated with chatter and giggles.

Nell unlinked her arm from the girl's upon seeing Dick. She ran, backpack bouncing upon her shoulders, into a warm hug.

"Hey! How was school?"

"Fine, the usual, David was an ass and decided to derail my reading of the creative piece we had to write over the Christmas break," Nell replied with a roll of her eyes.

They reached the car.

"Perhaps David was jealous of your fantastic storytelling?"

"Yeah, maybe, but it meant everyone missed the ending. It was pretty creepy. They would have liked it."

Dick smiled at Nell in the rearview mirror. She always had had a penchant for the macabre—sure, sometimes she went too far, as the concerned phone call from a previous teacher had suggested—but Dick maintained that witnessing your father be a victim of a hit and run was going to have an indelible impact. The distant screeching. The crunch of metal against flesh and bone. The smell of burning rubber on tarmac.

"What happens in the end?" Dick asked.

"The ghost the girl believed she was seeing all along was a real woman, stalking her. Obsessed with her. The idea came to me when I thought I'd seen Mu— I mean Jane hanging around but it turned out not to be her. And anyway, the school counsellor said it was common to imagine seeing a parent you are estranged from, because of the anxiety."

Nell continued to chew gum.

Imperceptible to Nell, Dick's eyes had widened. They hadn't heard from Jane for two years, not since she had tried to visit Dick in the hospital after the accident.

*

Nell didn't take long to change for the party. She had already chosen her outfit the evening before. She knew Dick wouldn't condone her wearing make-up; she knew he would never not see Nell as little Nell with her pigtails. She slipped a cheap magazine freebie lipgloss into her bag anyway. David could ruin her ghost story but he wasn't going to mock her. His favourite taunt was chanting 'Plain Jane' at her make-up-less face and boyish frame. She wondered if he knew about her mother and what had happened to her.

"I'm ready!" Nell called on her way down the stairs.

"Goodness... You look so grown up," Dick said, all watery-eyed.

Once again, Nell rolled her eyes.

"Come on..." Nell hauled him out of the house.

"Wait! The door!" Dick fumbled with the keys.

Nell heard the first and then the second bolt, accustomed to her father's need for bolted doors. She had begun to wonder if he was keeping things in or out as this routine became part of the house and its noises each night.

*

She was waiting in the hallway. The mirror there allowed her to check her suit. She had to look pristine, like she had her life together. Because she did. She knew she was perfect for the role. She was a dedicated and committed individual. They were bound to want her. She had even put a portfolio together, showcasing her experience.

She noticed sweat forming at her temples but she smiled, readjusted the leather satchel over her shoulder. She hoped she wouldn't have to wait much longer.

*

Dick switched the radio station once Nell had leapt out of the car with a teenage 'Bye, Dad!' Boston was playing and he relaxed in the seat, navigating the traffic with one hand on the gear stick, the other tapping the wheel.

The hallway light was on, as Dick had left it, in the logic burglars were less likely to target well-lit homes. He unbolted the door, smiling at the satisfying sound of each bolt coming loose.

*

She was masterful. She had outdone herself, she was sure of it. He had been surprised by how wonderful she looked—how smart, how driven and ready for work. The portfolio had left him speechless. Nell at the park. Nell's performance in the school production. Nell at the school gates. Nell in the garden. She'd been diligent. Not once had she let her charge out of her sight (except for tonight but it was a price she was willing to pay to secure her position). He could not deny she was made for this. She was an expert. She knew Nell's favourite colour. She knew her favourite shampoo brand. She knew Nell would put on lipgloss tonight. She knew Nell left a spare key beneath a flowerpot in the garden, against her father's wishes. This was when she was most persuasive. She explained to Dick how this house was a cage—how Nell was a songbird longing for freedom and if Dick would just give Jane the chance, she would be perfect.

When Dick tried to reach for the phone she stopped him. They were in the kitchen, Jane figured it had the best lighting to show him her portfolio. She could tell he was struggling, no doubt with his own actions and his inability to see Jane's proficiency in motherhood—no doubt he was realising what he had deprived Nell of and how selfish he had been in trying to keep Nell all to himself.

When Dick tried to scream, she stopped him. It was quick. Jane told herself it was for the best, Dick had tried his best but Nell deserved better, they both deserved better.

Dick sank further in the chair. A gurgling sound bubbled from his throat. Jane took the knife, slick with blood, to the sink. She would wash up later.

A Married Woman's Story: a response to Katherine Mansfield's 'A Married Man's Story'. – Kristiana Reed (she/her)

You perch at your writing desk, fingertips barely connecting with the polished wood. Every night, you assume I cannot feel you, beady eyed and silent, watching me, instead of writing. You assume with babe in arm and a sideboard of dishes, I couldn't possibly know what my husband's up to.

When I met you, everything I knew became null and void; my life was child's play and nothing more. You were an avid, aspiring writer and a man I knew my mother would love more than I would. I was nineteen, naive and numb to the world. So, I loved you. My entire chest swelled with a voracious desire to have you, own you and never share you...

Until last Autumn.

The baby has your eyes, beady and silent, welling slightly as I rock and toss until those same eyes begin to waiver and blink, slowly. Sleep... We sleep alone now, accompanied only by our separate thoughts.

You've picked up your pen again. On November 20th—all those years ago, you informed me I was your muse. The Greek nine had never been enough for you. Yet, as the waves lapped against the rocks, my curls fluttered in the coastal chill and you struggled to tear your eyes away from my face, I became your muse; for the first time in my life, I was good enough...

We are fortunate, we live comfortably and within our means. A well-known publishing house picked up a selection of short stories, you had a serial in a newspaper and your hometown forked out for a memoir. What of me? I've smiled, pressed your suit trousers and spit adjectives into the air when you've twiddled hair furiously between your fore-finger and thumb. I've collected postcards from all the places we've been lucky to visit; collected instead of sent because that requires a recipient. My mother got tired of postcards, preferring expensive perfume as your pay packet began to swell. My friends were left behind when I swapped the Friday roller-disco for the backseat of your car to watch the stars.

It's as if the baby is you reincarnate. He struggles to settle, shifts awkwardly in my arms as if repulsed by my touch. I shush, hush and stroke his downy curls whilst he turns purple, livid with the thought of me as his mother. You manage to settle him; it is the one time you leave that desk. To coo and burble with your son, for twenty minutes in twenty-four hours. I love you both, I'm sure of it. Not once did I ever consider the grass was greener.

Until last Autumn.

Becoming comfortable altered the man I met. You were handsome, charming and the suits you wore fit you in all the right places. I cast my eyes nonchalantly towards you; count the liver spots, frown lines and bulges below your chin and above your belt. I remind myself appearances mean very little. Until I remember the outside reflects the inside. The selfishness, gluttony, and misery. The selfishness, gluttony and misery all belong to me too. With powerful hands, mine were tied. My thirst for love, recognition, and five minutes away from this baby, quenched.

You must know it lasted only six weeks...six weeks of pure delusion, yet I was utterly lost; falling like Alice, deeper and deeper, spinning in twists and adoring every second. Adrenaline reawakened. You must know it wasn't the sex. He smiled, no...he acknowledged me as more than the other human being in the room. He looked past the stretch marks, the lines tying me to you and blew raspberries. He made me howl with laughter, he showed me films you thought were travesties, played me music you called crass. He wasn't you.

The baby is in bed, thanks to you. I'm left with the sideboard of dishes and my thoughts. For years, my thoughts were unadventurous, limited like my circle of friends, maternal nature, and aspirations. My thoughts were constrained to these four, thick brick walls where only your creativity thrives as the rest is stifled. My thoughts were those of my Mother– the woman who will always love you more than I do.

What Do You See When You Close Your Eyes? – Madeleine S. Cargile (she/her)

"What do you see when you close your eyes?"

Melody holds Clara's gaze for several seconds. If given the chance, Clara thinks she could stare into her friend's eyes for hours. They're a warm amber, like sunlight through a whiskey glass or honey dripping from a stem—

Melody blinks, and a broad smile splits her face. She laughs.

"God, does it really sound that stupid?"

It takes several seconds for Melody's words to register. Clara reels herself from the depths of her thoughts, the gears in her mind spinning. *What did she ask, again?* Clara shakes her head with a light chuckle. "Where did that come from?" she asks, avoiding the question.

Following her head, Melody twists the rest of her body to the side. The two girls are inches apart, separated only by rumpled sheets. Clara had long since mapped the red-orange, floral pattern; she and Melody had slept in them every other weekend for the past decade.

Melody and Clara have been inseparable since second grade. They met one fateful Tuesday when Melody offered Clara half of her peanut butter sandwich, and even better, the entirety of her company. From then on, the two girls have done everything together: from trying and failing at rollerblading to failing then passing statistics (by a *very* narrow margin. Math has never been Clara's strong suit).

"I dunno." Melody's eyes dart to the ceiling, to the glow-stars pasted there. The low, violet light of the room provides enough darkness for them to shine dimly. Clara smiles softly, remembering the time they hung them up.

It'd taken nearly two hours, five bottles of glue, and three step-stools to stick them all right. "I think I heard it somewhere in a movie," Melody says.

Clara smirks. "Another sappy romance?"

"Could it be anything else?"

Melody brushes back a loose strand of hair from her face. "Just try it, will you? It seems so poetic."

Rolling her eyes, Clara obliges.

Darkness consumes her vision.

Then there's light.

It comes first in pinpricks, as big as the glow-stars on the ceiling. They widen into saucer-sized holes, enough for Clara to make out a bright sky. Clara feels the sun against her skin, the grass between her toes...

Melody and Clara stand together in a flowering meadow. Vibrant red and orange blooms—matching the pattern of Melody's sheets—speckle the rich green.

Melody turns and offers Clara her hand.

Clara instantly accepts it.

When Melody takes her into a spin, Clara giggles. When she stops and holds her face, Clara tenses. When Melody brings her lips to hers, Clara melts. Clara draws back, and the scene splits. Now, the two girls stand next to a gurgling fountain. The flowers have snaked upwards to frame a luscious courtyard. Pearl-white dresses cover both Clara and Melody from neck to toe, skirts flaring out at their feet.

Melody's hands are in Clara's again, but instead of giggles, vows flow from Melody's lips. When she finishes, cheers erupt behind the two girls. *Our guests.* Clara doesn't spare them a glance. All she sees is Melody—

Clara blinks, and the two girls age ten years. Plates of half-eaten food litter a worn kitchen table. Their daughters push away what's left on theirs, their attention shifting to the red hair ribbons crumpled in their laps. The young girls dangle them in front of each other's faces, bursting into giggles each time one touches their noses.

An older Melody sighs and shoots Clara a glance. Melody manages a tired smile. Clara takes her hand—

Smooth skin wrinkles in Clara's grasp. Melody's hair grays to match it. The two girls must be near seventy now, with joints stiff and muscles spent. They can't manage much movement beyond the gentle rocking of their wooden porch chairs. The subtle glow of fireflies lights the dusky air of the treeline. Hand-in-hand, Clara and Melody sit together, gazing out at the view. Peace swells in Clara's heart, full and content.

Clara opens her eyes, and everything vanishes.

The two girls are seventeen again, laying across the same floral sheets under the same false stars.

Melody's smile shines just as bright as it did in Clara's dreams.

"Well?" Melody leans closer. "What did you see?"

Clara wants to say that she doesn't remember, that the vision has already slipped away from her. But the image refuses to fade, a vivid stillness against the waters of Clara's mind. Her heart aches.

Before she can push some lie from her mouth, Clara catches a shift in Melody's eyes. Something has changed between the two girls; a tension clings to the edges of Clara's perception. Melody's amber eyes stay fully on her, taking in every speck of Clara's appearance.

"You." The word escapes Clara's lips before she can catch it. Panic floods Clara's mind. *God, what have you—*

Everything stops when Clara notices Melody's smile.

"I see you too," Melody agrees, grin widening, "I see us. Together." Snaking through sheets, her hand finds Clara's. Melody clasps it tightly. "Though, you look prettier when my eyes are open." Her gaze shifts to Clara's lips. "And, I've been wondering if the same goes for kissing you."

Clara's face heats. Her lips twist, unable to contain her smile. "Why don't we find out?"

The two girls closed their eyes, lips meeting in darkness. Sparks burst before Clara's blacked-out view, flooding her with light.

"Do You Like Me Now?" – Madeleine S. Cargile (she/her)

Do you like me now?

The question snakes down my spine. I flinch at the sensation, a chilled prickling. I run my fingers through freshly straightened hair, still singing with heat. It's all I can do to keep my hands from twitching.

Do you like me now?

The bathroom mirror reflects a face painted in perfect precision. Each eyeliner wing is identical, crisp and narrow, and there's not a hint of a smudge of lipstick. Thick layers of foundation cover blotchy, botched skin. I can feel its redness in my cheeks and heaviness under my eyes, but it's invisible on the surface. *And isn't that all that matters in the end?*

Do you like me now?

I'd never ask the question aloud.

You shouldn't have to ask it at all, a quiet voice adds, a mere whisper of the strength she used to feed me.

She used to be loud.

She was loud when I was young, a small girl with grass-stained pants and pigtails. All I cared about was how fast I could run and how many bugs I could catch. I never gave my appearance a second thought: clothes were clothes, and I was who I was.

She quieted some when I hit thirteen. I knew clunky braces and acne weren't the cutest look, but I'd always spent more time reading books than obsessing over makeup or boys. The pages couldn't see me anyways, and my friends loved me regardless.

She went silent when I met him.

Him—with his casual look and easy smile. Him—with his dazzling eyes and flowing, low voice. He swept me off my feet with kind words and grand gestures. In the beginning, I couldn't imagine a more perfect guy.

But, apparently, he could imagine a more perfect me.

It was little things at first. *Why don't you wear a bit more makeup when we go out? No, not that much, something more natural. Your hair would look so pretty straightened.* I obliged at first—I mean, they were easy fixes. And if that was all he wanted to be a bit happier with me...

Do you like me now?

That's when the question was born, wasn't it? A cyst seeping into a cesspool, poisoning my mind from within.

Do you like me now?

Will my red-stained lips earn a smile from him?

Do you like me now?

Are my plain, short clothes enough to soften his eyes?

Do you like me now?

Is my powdered face enough to spare me from his anger?

Do you like me now?

Is it enough to dry my tears?

On that last thought, my lips trembled. I force them into a smile to mask my pain. I meet my reflection's gaze.

No, the voice inside me answers, *It was never enough. You will never be enough for him.*

A beat passes, and it adds:

You never should've had to be perfect for him.

I let my smile drop. The tension in my face leaches to my hands. With a flood of force, I snatch a towel from the rack. After dousing it with water, I drag it over my face. Creams and powders blend into sludge. Black liner streaks from cheek to cheek. It's a horridly delightful mess.

I do my best to clear my skin of the worst of it. What's left are shadows; gray rings my eyes—redness, my cheeks and chin. There's a strange lightness to my face, freed from the weight of more than just makeup.

Do you like me now?

A laugh escapes me. The girl in the mirror is nothing near society's image of pretty. She's not perfect or pristine. *But she's me.* That, in itself, was its own type of beauty— not something draped in gilded glitter, but something raw, something true.

The question remains, but its presence has been cleaved by streaks from the towel. It's as quiet as my confidence was just minutes ago.

Do you like me now? It whispers. It's no longer aimed at any man, but solely at me.

When I meet my gaze in the mirror, I can finally say yes.

Animal – PD Hogan (he/him)

But the animal itself, the father never would have let the child play with it. Its fur, matted and dirty, seeped the rain from the previous night when she squeezed it. It had rained the year before too, he remembered. Everyone remembered.

And the car had long been pulled from the creek, but the saplings that grew along its edges were still bent in half, trying to survive with what water they could get when the creek was high enough. This time of year, it was always high enough.

But one year later and here were waterlogged candles and flowers, the blackened sky and intentionless winds pulling and threatening to interfere.

And this animal could have been one from last night or one from last year, the father wasn't sure, but regardless, it didn't belong to her—although who did it belong to? What was the timeline for when a roadside memorial becomes litter?

But she's not asking for permission anymore, holding it out to him. No, she's squeezing it against herself, her sweater soaking as the animal squelches, drips onto the sidewalk, a mildewed smell entering the air even in these low temperatures.

And he tries to take it from her, at first with a gentle hand, then with a firmer one, his hand growing cold and wet and tired as he tugs at the arm, just enough held back not to harm it, but she screams all the same and he has to pull harder and she screams louder and now people are looking. Should he just let her have it for now? Try to clean it or throw it away when they're home?

But no, she's already soaked to her flesh and her mittens will be just as damp and she'll start shivering soon and it's still another thirty-minute walk home, so he gives it one last good yank and it slides from her grip. Defeated, she cries, not trying to get it back but retreating into herself and the father walks back to the collection of artifacts and tries to find somewhere to place it but he's not sure where he can that doesn't feel like he's overtaking it or isolating it, and besides, he sees the child eyeballing it, waiting for him to put it down so she can snatch it up again.

And he looks to the creek and swears he can still see tire marks in the mud, but those had long been flattened, and the sound of the child is overtaken by the water as he tosses it in and doesn't even wait to hear the splash.

Teeth – PD Hogan (he/him)

When the first tooth breaks I think little of it. Teeth do break, after all. So I go to the dentist, who refers me to an orthodontist, who refers me to a cosmetic dentist, who charges me more than the first two combined to install a veneer. A fake incisor that stands out worse than when it was broken, all clean and white and porcelain. He tells me to stay away from hard foods and I should be fine. That the rest of my teeth look strong. Floss and brush twice a day, he tells me. Okay, I lie.

The thing I don't tell him, tell any of them, is that my jaw hurts from grinding my teeth at night. Not even when I'm asleep. I just sit there, staring at the TV or maybe out the window and work my jawbone. It makes my ears ring all day and sometimes the next time I eat, it's like chewing a handful of sand. But with my new tooth, I tell myself maybe I'll try to stop.

It works for a little bit until I stop paying attention and catch myself doing it again, and who knows how long I've been doing it, except my fillings feel hot so probably a little while, so I bite down as hard as I can, preventing any movement, only that hurts worse. The sides of my tongue are rubbed raw and sometimes I think I can taste blood except the last few years I feel like I can barely taste anything at all, so I just hold my mouth open.

My jaw still moves through the air and my tongue starts to hurt more with the exposure. There's salt in the kitchen, big rock salt, so I pour some in because I can't tell if blood is starting to pool in my mouth or if it's just extra spit but I'm too afraid to check, like I don't trust my own jaw not to bite off my finger in revenge, but the rock salt is sharp and now my eyes are watering and my mouth is too dry, like the kind of dry you feel when you suck your teeth, that cold air dry where all you want to do is close your mouth, so I do and I bite down on all that salt and it shatters and scrapes across everything. And I'm drinking water, first from a glass and then straight from the tap, and I'm swishing it around and adding more salt and crunching it and my tongue is burning and I think I'm outright crying now.

My gums feel like they're bleeding too and my mouth is dry from the salt but I keep pouring water in to make up for it until my stomach starts to hurt, but at this point I'm not sure if there's even salt left or if I broke another tooth, or maybe all my teeth, except I know my new one still stands tall and proud because my tongue shoots out to check its condition and for a brief and glorious moment, I feel safe before biting clean through.

THE MAGE'S APPRENTICE – Estelle Grace Tudor (she/her)

The winter mists roll in, swirling around my ankles as I walk, bringing with it the scent of snow. My thin cloak drags along the mossy forest floor soaking the hem, and I struggle over broken twigs and fallen logs, the urgency to rectify my mistake making me clumsy. The wand given to me by the mage glows softly in my red, chafed hand, numb from the bitter cold. A cold I cannot acknowledge; I must carry on or my family will perish.

A branch snaps beneath my boot with a crack, echoing through the forest, causing a murder of crows to erupt from the barren tree to my left. I stumble and nearly drop the wand, barely hanging onto it with my frozen claw-like fingers. Through my trembling lips a sob escapes, the sound shocking me, eerie in the stillness.

The pale winter sun's dying rays filter weakly through the trees and my breath hitches.

Time is running out.

Spurred on, I wrestle to push down my fear but tied to my emotions, power flows through me causing the wand to pulse in my hand. I take a moment to calm my swirling thoughts as I have been taught. This is not the time for more accidental spells.

I see a movement, and I sense my quarry. Fear becomes determination and I turn, there he stands, observing me from across the glass-like pond, shrouded by the bare trees. His dark eyes meet mine, and for a moment, we are connected. I feel his silent plea, and I utter an apology because I have no choice. This is not nature's way; I have dabbled with the fragile balance and now creatures walk on two feet and men howl in the night.

His eyes never leave mine as I walk towards the edge of the pond, poised for chase, but still, he doesn't move. I instinctively know he's aware his time has come. This charade must come to an end. I aim the wand and say the spell, the words whipped away from my frozen lips by the icy wind and carried across the pond. His image ripples and wavers before disappearing, leaving only a pile of clothes and a handsome red fox. With a last longing look at the clothes from his cunning black eyes, he slinks away into the mist.

I sag as my power dissipates, leaving me a hollow shell. Relief courses through me, filling the void, as the realisation hits that I have changed back all the enchanted creatures; the curse should be broken! I must return to the castle, but I quail at the thought. In showing off my new-found magic to my friend Princess Marietta, I may have created enemies in other quarters.

The air shifts and dead leaves swirl around me funneling up into the darkening sky. With a crack the mage appears before me. Pushing my tangled black hair away from my face, I meet his sardonic gaze.

"So, you managed to restore the balance in time. The king and his sons are safely returned to men." I breathe a sigh of relief at his statement.

"And my family?" I ask hesitantly, my teeth chattering. I hold out the wand, knowing in my heart that I would not be permitted to use it for a while, perhaps indefinitely. Being the mage's apprentice came with responsibility and it had been folly to think I could arrogantly cast spells without consequences.

My mentor pauses before taking the wand and tucking it in the pocket of his star-strewn cloak. "No harm will come to your family—" he stops, and I wait for his next words nervously, "but the king has demanded your presence."

My heart stutters, my earlier thoughts were correct; I fear my friendship with the king's daughter will not be enough to save me this time.

The mage notices my pale face and says, "Where is your bravery now, girl?"

Resolutely I stop trembling and look into his aged eyes. "I'm sorry, I never meant for this to happen.

"Tell that to the king. Come." With an intricate move of his staff, the mage whisks us away from the forest.

I open my eyes and see we are now stood outside the castle walls. I follow slowly behind as the mage enters the open gateway. Suddenly, I'm whirled away from the entrance and into an alcove of the wall.

Princess Marietta lowers the hood of her blue cloak to reveal her face. She thrusts a pouch of coins into my still numb hands and unfastens her cloak. "Swap with me," she murmurs urgently.

"What are you doing? My family—" I stutter in confusion.

"Are safe. I had my most trusted man-at-arms take them into the next kingdom. You must join them there. Your life is in danger." Marietta makes quick work of securing my black cloak around her and pulling up the hood. "Please go, it is my fault you cast that spell."

Still, I pause. "I cannot allow you to risk yourself for me," I say.

"I'll be fine; they'll not harm me," she says with confidence and a touch of contempt.

"Girl!" The mage's impatient voice flutters out of the gateway.

"Go now," Marietta urges, and I nod. "Thank you," I whisper. She waits until I slip back into the trees, before walking slowly through the entrance, her head bowed, and her distinctive hair covered by the hood. How much time she has bought me I don't know, so I hasten along the familiar path I traversed earlier but this time I'm warmer thanks to Marietta's fur-lined cloak.

Panic clutches at my heart, as the path leading to the next kingdom becomes shrouded in mist. Slowly, the panic recedes as a pair of familiar eyes glow in the dark.

"This way," a silky voice coaxes, and with a flick of a bushy red tail, I recognise the fox. Trusting my instincts, I follow him into the night and towards my future.

Bathwater – Jordan Nishkian (she/her)

You once heard that you could figure out which way was up by following the bubbles.

You weren't sure when it had started, but the tinnitus that haunted your right ear had now wrapped around your head and entered your left. At first, it was something you only heard in silence—now there were days when the ringing was nearly debilitating.

You pushed through work until the new guy with the compass tattoo relieved your shift in the parking lot attendant booth. Summer was over; even at four, the sky left you wanting for daylight.

The thirty-minute walk home was littered with crescendos of ringing in your ears—aggravated by squealing tires and blasts of bass-heavy music—but it quieted down by the time your heavy feet trudged up the stairs to your studio apartment.

Though it had been two months since Mara moved out, you were half expecting to hear the chatter from one of her shows when you opened your door. You didn't miss her need for noise, but you did miss the bread she learned to bake by watching British people compete for a cake stand, the superstitious habits she developed when she watched something too scary, the lack of space she left on your walls. You missed how she could sing along to any song.

You never noticed the ringing until she left—maybe there was something to her strategy.

Eight hours in the attendant booth left you with a film of stale exhaust settling into your skin. The patter of water in the shower was usually the only type of ambient distraction that could appease the ringing, but perhaps it was the steam.

You reached your arm behind the clear plastic shower curtain and turned the water-spotted knob. A rattle in the pipes released a sluggish trickle from the showerhead. After weeks of warning, the shower arm had finally given out on you.

You tried your luck with the tub faucet, smacking down the calcified peg that directed water to your now-useless showerhead. Tepid water flowed out of the teal-tinged tap, and once it warmed up a bit, you pressed down on the drain stopper until you felt it click into place.

The water crashing into the acrylic tub became a part of the city soundtrack as you walked across the apartment to the kitchen. You dried your hand on a rumpled-up towel on the counter and glanced over your uninspired pantry, opting to pour yourself half a mug of the black spiced rum Mara left behind.

The ringing swelled, but before your hand could reach your ear, it quieted. It was still there, but not as sharp, like the reverberation after striking a bell. You swallowed the contents of your novelty mug without setting it down, flooding your throat with a slow-draining burn that was quick to seep into your lungs and your stomach.

The rum did nothing for the humming, but it helped your memory.

You set the empty mug on the counter and made your way back to the tub, stepping out of your scuffed sneakers and taking off your navy-polo-and-black-pants uniform. You left your clothes in a pile by your bed, noticing that the hum was getting louder by the time your bare feet felt the linoleum.

You pulled the curtain aside and turned off the tap, testing the temperature with your hand before stepping into the overfilled tub. Easing your body into the water caused it to slosh over the edge and onto the floor, instantly soaking the dollar-store bath mat beside it.

The warmth of the water was forgiving and lent you a feeling of lightness that you hadn't felt in years. Small waves rocked you, and you began finding rhythms in the hum. Eyes closed, you tilted your head back until your ears filled with bathwater. You expected the sound to be muffled and cloudy, but it only became clearer and more familiar.

Your fingers curled around the edge of the tub as you pulled yourself up from under the surface. Your eyes darted around the bathroom—you were alone and her humming had softened. Easing your spine against the wall of the tub, you let your eyes close again, trying to block out the sound with the gentle lapping of warm water against the walls of the tub. The steam rose and collected around your nose and across your brow. Despite your best efforts, her melody lingered in your mind and beckoned you to listen.

Lungs filled, you prepared to submerge yourself. You lowered your face into the water, greeted by the sound of her voice. Your body sunk into the weightlessness as you opened your eyes, looking for the source of the song. Soft yellow light poured in from your ceiling, and there was nothing to see besides your own blurred limbs.

Your lids lowered closed as you began moving your arms to the tune of her voice. The places where your vertebrae anchored you to the floor of the tub detached until each part of you was swaddled in water.

Legs outstretched, you started to kick, feeling self-initiated currents pummel between your toes. The darkness behind your eyelids embedded you in the rise and fall of her otherworldly pitch and the push and pull of the water, which had grown colder.

You arched your back and paddled your limbs in circles. Small whirlpools churned behind your knees and shoulders. You felt a freedom in expanding, in feeling your muscles stretch out in a glorious yawn after being confined to the limitations of concurrent compartmentalization.

Her song became louder, and you felt a neighboring current swirl around you. You swore her fingers were interlacing yours, that her hair was painting waves over your shoulders and chest.

You opened your eyes, and in the split second you could bear the burn of salt, you saw you were swallowed in openness—still alone, feeling your lungs pinch and contract with deprivation. You clawed for the walls of the tub, but all you could sense was a cold and briny expanse. Forcing your eyes open, you found yourself lost in indigo—a directionless space with no division of light and dark.

You once heard that you could figure out which way was up by following the bubbles.

Ready to kick, you unsealed your lungs, hoping your last small ration of air could lead you to the surface.

Broken Record – Gabrielle Pelayo (she/her)

He is a broken record.

Not like he wanted to be. He's covered in scratches and cracks against his will. He had been new at one point, as all things begin, and he did his best to keep himself in pristine condition. The environment, however, has ways of destroying even the most precious of things. The ones that no one would dare mess with are still just as susceptible to damage.

He's fragile now, more than he used to be. He is an artifact that cannot sustain any more damage. Yet even today he takes too many hits. The cracks grow longer and deeper. The scratches, ever increasing in number.

Yet he refuses to show it. He fills the cracks and paints over the scratches with a strong presence and very limited emotions. Many people don't know he is not in mint condition. They just think he's...a little awkward, is all; the track skips but they pay no mind. "Delivery is a bit clumsy," he'll lie through adamant eyes, and they eat it up. "Sorry for the damage. I guarantee you won't find any problems other than that."

But the people that can see through his fraudulent sales pitch take the skips to heart. They can see under the paint job and pick out the scratches. They pick away at the painted over glue filling the cracks and peel it out, exposing them. And they've found that the skipping lyrics are a cry for help that slips under our noses. Those with a musical ear even note the sour melody that was advertised as melodious and clean.

He's aware that people have discovered his dirty secret. He'd attempted in the past to find a professional to repair him. Some could not do much, others did nothing at all. Even when he thought he was fixed, he discovered more mysterious scratches appearing. He's uncomfortable with the way he is, how sour his melody is, how those who hear his true tune and see him for who he really is turn their backs.

But I was one who wanted to help repair him.

I will admit, I was one to pass off his out of key melody as just a slight error, thinking it would correct itself. I fell for his sales pitch, unaware of the scam.

"Nah, I'm alright."
"I'm fine, really."
"I'm just a bit of a weirdo."

I didn't trust my intuition and believed the lyrics for their surface level meaning. I conducted a quick consultation at one point early on—wanted to judge the damage for myself—and figured there was nothing severe or too damaging. "It'll fix itself," I'd recommend. Yet now I feel that I was more telling myself that than telling him, sort of as a comfort.
He knows himself better than anyone. He *is* the broken record, after all. He's aware of his damage. His attempts to play it off as social awkwardness when there's a skip or a wrong note; he already knows. Don't remind him of those surface level scratches. And he knows that the damage is more internal than it seems. Those cracks, they dive deep. Sooner or later, he's gonna collapse, lose his integrity, his tune will be no more.

The broken record, he's built walls. Whenever someone mishandles him, the wall grows a layer. Sometimes it's taller, sometimes it's thicker; whatever the case may be, it becomes more impenetrable. He doesn't let anyone in, and he's hesitant to come out. I know this because he told me himself. The broken record seems to trust me, at least enough to admit the severity of his damage.

"I've been damaged for years," he explained. "About sixth grade or so."

I met him when *I* was in seventh, so he was in eighth when we first came across one another. His first impression was, apparently, deceiving; he didn't appear to be damaged. I didn't notice any scratches, cracks, or skipping tracks. The tune played almost perfectly, save for a hiccup or two that I didn't seem to notice.

"So the boy I met on the bus in junior high," I said, the realization hitting me. "Who was that?"

"That wasn't me. At least, not the real me."

Mental health, anger, loss, and ADHD were the hidden themes in the tune he played. Yet when an oblivious music lover would set him on the turntable and drop the needle, they'd only be concerned about the words themselves: a short temper, video games, and a relatively quiet social life that became quite the opposite when online. The oblivious heard verses of acting, cooking, and playing in marching band. They were intrigued by his vast knowledge of military history that was prevalent throughout the melody. His wild laughter put them in a good mood and made them unaware of the pain conveying itself through hidden meaning.

In reality, I had met the broken record when he was already quite broken.

"I took the black eyes that were meant for others," he explained as he showed me the various scratches and cracks on his vinyl surface. "I stood up for others only for them to turn their backs. And when they talked back, I couldn't help but get angry whether I liked it or not. And it's made it difficult to befriend others. I hate myself, I'm mad at myself, and I wish I could be better but I just can't."

As I listen to his tune again and again, the message becomes clearer. Every skip has a meaning. The sour melody doesn't sound so sour to me anymore. Through the joyous laughter, reminiscent of more youth-filled days, and hopes for the future contained within the lyrics, I can pick apart the layers and read the subtext. His walls are tall and heavy. He suffers from loss and is still trying to recover from the ones that did him wrong. He spends his days keeping to himself, keeping the emotions built up behind that wall, and carrying himself as someone strong—your typical male stereotype. He's afraid of losing those he loves; it's his sworn duty to protect them. Life is, as for anyone, fairly challenging. Through the skips in the track, his melody speaks of those hidden emotions he is afraid of letting others see: fear, distress, and his true degree of anger.

You know, I no longer wish to fix the broken record.

Because after hearing it all from him personally, there is no fixing him. No immediate attention nor natural repairs performed by time can ever truly buff out the scratches and fill the cracks. That melody—well, it wouldn't be the same.

Something about those skips—how the needle grazes along those grooves, how it struggles to hop over the scratches and cracks—is alluring to me. The damage makes him...unique, even if he is a little awkward. It makes him appear closed off, like he wants nothing to do with you, but that is because he is afraid to speak up. Open up to the broken record, and I guarantee he will open up to you. Isn't that how it works with most people?

I have a new appreciation for the broken record now that I understand where his damage comes from. It is beautiful, and I want him to embrace it. I love that damaged vinyl with all my heart. I will set him on the turntable and listen to him every day. I have come to enjoy the skips, the cracks, the wear and tear both seen and unseen. Because no one is perfect; not one person has walked through life without taking a beating.

He is a broken record, but aren't we all a little broken?

NON-FICTION

Heaven Has a Broken Door – Brendaliz Torres (she/her)

Mi papa doesn't process emotion. I can't remember the last time he cried. When he received the call from Puerto Rico that his stepfather passed, it was brief. His voice wasn't smothered in grief. Your death was anticlimactic in our home.

Abuelo Güigüi's mustache danced with his words, his arm branded with a lone name-in-a heart tattoo that tarnished green. The jingle of his keys when he played with them in his pocket. How skinny he was and how my fingers, inevitably, found each other when I hugged him. His staccato cough from cigarette-infused lungs. Still, I hear him whistling.

I can't picture the last life of him. His eyes swimming in their sockets. Or, if his bones over-stretched his skin. I can't visualize an all-white mustache. If I closed my eyes to see the fragility of him, the mosaic would never be complete. How did the world sound without his whistling?

Bits of him, most of him, not enough of him.

Is it true? Were you hearing the loosening thread of worry in my voice when I spoke of my fears? Did you feel the building stress inside of my chest? Who tried to fool my unconsciousness? If a dream is a dream and you're dead, did I die a little or did you breathe again?

Then, you found the broken door. All I had to do was sleep.

***

My father cut the engine in the middle of a dead street. Our van didn't belong. Neither did we. I had no idea where I was, but I didn't hesitate when the side door slid open. Fingers peeked through, head, legs, then the rest of me. The stars waved, winked, kissed me. I'd never seen the night prove its infinity. I was lucky to see it so sprinkled.

Endless monotony. Every house was identical from paint color, to flowers in the garden claiming the same amount of land. Moths danced under the lit light posts. We were proof that life existed on this nameless street.

We stood in the middle of lazy suburbia.

In a circle, we waited. I watched the stars some more, hid the nape of my neck. One of the house doors opened, bright white light poured past the stairs and sidewalk to our feet. An elderly couple brought more life to the street. The light hid the stars. A woman made her way to us, a man followed. Like my whereabouts, they looked unfamiliar. Their skin, ghostlike in the dark. She wore a thin, quilted jacket, and her hair rolled into a bun. I fixated on her.

Without a word, she reached for my father and hugged him first. He folded into her. His tears were rough, forming waves in her hair. She stood firm under my father. The stars couldn't pull my eyes back up. I focused on the unknown street, couple, sound of my crying father.

Then, she hugged my mother. Mami began to cry. This, I was familiar with. I've wiped her tears, understood her when she spoke in garbled gibberish. I lifted her pants when her knees trembled, pulled a top over her head and arms.

Each hug was intimate. Both bodies blended until they began to shudder.

The couple's other half stood a distance away with both hands in his trousers' pockets. His hands moved up-and-down-around, up-and-down-around. From the corner of my eye, I saw my father hug him.

I followed the woman's steps, without missing any of her movements. The stars coated her skin, she glowed, and yet, I saw her features without having to squint. Her presence overwhelmed me once she stood in front of me. In an instant, I became teary-eyed. Still, I couldn't recognize her. She wrapped her hands over my upper back, where angel wings stem. With my arms tucked under hers, the street dazed and dimmed. When she let go of me, I felt cold. My features tensed, building, and waiting for a teary release.

When the man stepped in front of me, I expected to see a stranger. But a trigueño, slim man with slicked-back hair, and a thick mustache stood in front of me.

Mi abuelo. Mi Güigüi.

Without hesitation, I hugged him tight, our ribcages interlocked. Chemicals of his hairspray filled my nostrils. The indent of his mini hair comb peeked from his back pocket. He tucked a crisp white Hanes tank top into a pair of grey trousers. A black leather belt held his pants around his skinny waist. His shoes glistened like the stars. My eyebrows were dancing, my smile lines tugged at each other pushing to release the sobs. His shirt stretched into my fists, wrinkles in my knuckles became nonexistent. I wanted to know what he was doing on this street, this darkness, in my world again.

"How are you here?"

No answer, but you held me.

"Why are you here?"

No answer, but you smiled at me.

"Are you okay?"

Then, I woke up.

I was in my bedroom under string lights, instead of stars. Already, forgetting the expanse of the night sky. The tears dripped from my chin. You weren't in this room with me. I wasn't on the dead street. I must've visited the place where Earth meets beyond what we know. One of my angels found a way to hide his wings, dim his halo, and sneak through the stars to see me. Heaven wasn't far, at all.

I close my eyes, again, and am covered in green. Then, I see you. Puerto Rico's wild, open, loud land is your backdrop. You are whistling in front of the *casita*. Salsa makes the curtains dance.

You're happy you found me.

Keep Families Together – Savannah Verdin (she/her)

Biologically humans are wired to bond with their mothers, and the neurobiological processes for that bonding begin in the womb. This is why all adoption is developmental trauma, even when the child is adopted at birth. How much, and in what way, these traumas manifest are as different and unique as each adoptee, and some may not feel it at all, but grief is in their bones and fight or flight is in their nervous systems.

The reality is, there are far more hopeful adoptive parents in the United States than there are children needing adoption, and the majority are those hoping to adopt a newborn. I believe that, as long as this is the case, and there is money to be made, there will always be unethical people, agencies, and practices to meet the demand. This must change. Children are not commodities that can be acquired. There really is no need for more adoptive parents. If you want to help a child, do something to support a parent in raising a child. Many wouldn't choose adoption if they had the emotional support and financial resources to parent. Oftentimes, relinquishments happen due to poverty and misfortune. Women who've experienced violence and landed in desperate and vulnerable positions can still want to parent. The abuse they experienced doesn't and won't make them a bad parent. If they have an immediate family and support system that doesn't support their right to parent, it doesn't mean that they shouldn't parent. The fear they experience during a new and/or unplanned pregnancy doesn't mean they don't want to parent or shouldn't. Poverty shouldn't be criminalized. Misfortune shouldn't be capitalized on. If you want to help, become a foster parent who does everything they can to support children in returning to their family. This is how you do what's in the best interests of the child/children. If you want to help, give birth parents who inquire (or that are sought out) an opportunity to have all of the information. Let them speak to adoptees who are allowed to tell their truth without being attached to an agency or organization that filters what they say. Let them speak to birth mothers who are allowed the same space to be honest without any pressure of helping agencies acquire and convince vulnerable parents with an only positive narrative. There's a huge misconception that biological parents who place don't want to parent, but to be very candid, I signed with tears in my eyes, falling to the signature line, all while being rushed through the process. This isn't consent, is it?

I am not anti-adoption, but I do promote family preservation as a birth mother who's experienced systems in our society fail to promote and support family preservation. In regard to foster care, the primary goal should always be family preservation. Caseworkers should do everything possible to support that goal. People signing on to foster parent should not do so with the goal of a more affordable path to adoption. With that said, private adoptions should not coerce, manipulate, pressure, and lead vulnerable biological families into placement by threatening foster placements and child protective services reports in order to finalize signatures to obtain a child/children. This is one of many tactics used to coerce signatures once biological parents doubt placing.

In my experience, I survived domestic violence and attained temporary two-year housing that lasted the duration of court hearings while battling safety and advocating for the wellbeing of both my children and I. I walked away with final custody and a permanent restraining order. At the end of that two-year period despite seeking other options, pursuing programs, and going as far as volunteering to make connections, we were vulnerable and struggling to find housing. This is where I surrendered parental rights. Society villainizes birth parents and makes poverty and being a victim of abuse into a personal failure when it is in fact a system failure.

A mother who parented for over eight years and doesn't have her children somehow translates into "an abusive mother", "an inadequate mother", amongst other unsolicited feedback I've received. And adoptive parents are seen as saviors and saints because they had the resources and a desire to adopt. Should we unpack that?

Some people with religious beliefs say that god called them to adopt. I believe that people feel inspired by the god of their faith, but I don't believe that adoption is god's perfect plan for any child. I in no way want to disrespect anyone's belief systems, but to me this feels like saying that god placed a child in the wrong womb simply to experience a trauma in order to get them to the right family, and that doesn't seem like a kind or just god. Obviously, this isn't the only reason you'll hear adoptive parents give, but it is at the core of adoption trauma and it's a weight that makes adoptees feel as though they shouldn't feel grief or wonder about and desire a connection to their biology.

I am just one part of a triad, but I've sat a long while with my own grief and the decisions and events that resulted in adoption. I've dissected and sought explanations and reasons. I've wanted to understand how my decision impacted my children and the only way I've seen to do this is by speaking with adoptees who've experienced this. I've sought conversations with adoptive parents and contemplated their part in it. I've found there's a disconnect about the knowledge we have regarding what adoptees go through and have experienced. With this, I want to encourage you to read this with an open mind and heart and consider the possibility that adoption isn't a blessing. Again, I am in no way anti-adoption, but adoption isn't the only solution, nor should it be the first option, especially if there are other areas we can triage and support in order to prevent it.

The last thing I'll say is that in cases of adoption being a necessity, there should be no secrecy in adoption. On the outside of adoption, you wouldn't know about the secrecy or what it's like to have your biology buried and hidden from you. These individuals wouldn't conclude or know that adoptees have to have their initial birth certificate legally changed, won't experience the feelings of betrayal at not having access to their history, often resulting in their biology ultimately being erased in order for them to have their basic needs met. This shouldn't be the case, but it won't be defined as the developmental trauma that it is unless a part of the adoption triad helps inform outsiders of this. Secrecy and similar restrictions can even come up in open adoptions. When the open relationship is micromanaged and limited, it withholds certain information and prevents authenticity of sincere relationships between adoptees and biological families. A relationship should have a natural flow, and like adoption, anything restrictive of this goes up against the natural intention of human existence. Outsiders wouldn't think about how being lied to about your identity and the adoption only contributes to the trauma. Adoptees have every right to know the identity of their first parents, siblings, and extended family. In addition, siblings and extended family have a right to know the existence and identity of a child placed for adoption. Adult adoptees should have easy and full access to unchanged records of their birth, as well as their original birth certificate. Currently, that is not the case. They have every right to know their identity and heritage just like anyone else. Secrecy and attempts to control the narrative prevent adoptees from knowing the truth and having an opportunity to develop their own feelings and thoughts about it.

Adoptees weren't given a decision in the placement, and we should work to empower adoptees and become alliances in elevating their voices.

ABOUT THE CONTRIBUTORS

❖ Abbey Lynne Rays is a poet and educator living in the California Bay Area. Her work has appeared in several publications including *Havik: Journal of Arts and Literature, Viewless Wings Publication, Beyond Word Magazine, and Free Verse Revolution Magazine.* When she is not writing she enjoys hiking, traveling and soaking in the scenery of Northern California. You can connect with her on her Instagram @a.l.rays

❖ adam Shove is an Estonian English poet, who writes poems laden with cryptic metaphors and pop culture references; doused in vodka and thrift shop ideas. Inspired by RZA, Frank Ocean, secondhand clothes, models, tattoos and expensive cars. Find him on Instagram @thepoetshove

❖ Alexis Hernandez is an aspiring musical theater performer, and dreamer. Her original play was a finalist in the *2020 California Young Playwrights Competition.* She is pursuing an English degree with dreams of becoming an English teacher, writer, and performer.

❖ Alice Carroll lives in the midwest and writes poetry. Sometimes, she gets paid for it.

❖ Alice Whiting has three poems in the current *Sunday Mornings at The River Spring Anthology.* Her poetry appears in the latest issue of *Soft Quarterly Magazine* and has been previously published by *Versification Zine, The New River Press, Dear Damsels, She is Fierce Magazine* and *The Sunday Times.* Alice lives in Berlin. Twitter: alicehwhiting

❖ Amanda Brown is a digital content writer moonlighting as a poet in St. Louis. Amanda's work has been published in *Word & Whispers* magazine and she has 3 poems forthcoming in an upcoming anthology by *Sunday Mornings at the River.*

❖ Amanda Karch is a Babson College alum, honing her entrepreneurship skills through her journey as a poet and author. She self-published a poetry collection, *Her Favorite Color Was Sunshine Yellow,* selling almost 200 copies in its first print year. Her debut nonfiction book, *Poetic Potential: Sparking Change & Empowerment Through Poetry,* released in December 2021 through *New Degree Press,* and it is her hope to spread the power of poetry and of female voices to the world. You can find her on social media (Instagram & Twitter) @akkwriting.

❖ Amelia Jacob is an English Literature student. When she is not writing overly long text messages, she is scribbling short stories.

- Asher Phoenix was born and raised in Illinois. She was born with a rare disability called Arthrogryposis Multiplex Congenita. She had her struggles, but they didn't stop her from living a "normal" life. Asher is a quirky, sarcastic, and funny person with a big heart. She published her debut book, *Kaleidoscope* on October 29, 2020. It was one of her greatest accomplishments. She lets the ink bleed within the lines about her mental health, love, her sexuality, and the struggles and triumphs of having a disability.

- Basil is a poet and a graphic designer. They enjoy fantasy and storytelling. This is their first published work. More of their writing can be found on Instagram @insanepoetics where they share poetry and prose.

- Bharti Bansal is a 24 year old poet from India. She has her works published in magazines like *Aaduna, sunflowercollective, selcouth station, oc87recoverydiaries.org* and others. She loves cats, poetry, and universe. She hopes to write her own book someday.

- Brendaliz Torres is born and raised in Jersey City, NJ. She has a BA in Creative Writing. She is an independently published author of *Faceless Lovers, Ghosts, for Now*. She, also, works as a Luxury Fashion Authenticator for a leading reconsignment company.

- Carlos Clark is from Milwaukee, WI. He has been an artist for 15 years and loves to create in many disciplines. Mainly a poet and short story writer, he also enjoys painting and taking photos when given the chance.

- Christina Hennemann is a writer based in the beautiful West of Ireland. Her work has appeared in *orangepeel, Anti-Heroin Chic, Goats Milk, Free Verse Revolution, Tír na nÒg, Hecate* and elsewhere. Her first poetry book is forthcoming. Christina writes about the subconscious mind, trauma, the healing power of nature and spirituality, relationships and the anxiety that sometimes comes with them. Find her on Instagram @c.h_92

- Christina D. Rodriguez is a Latina poet, entrepreneur, and woman of tech from New York, currently living in Chicago. Her poems have appeared in various online and print journals and anthologies. Christina has received awards for *the Frost Place Conference on Poetry* and *Winter Tangerine's Catalyze Self-Revolutions* workshop. She is a board member of the Chicago Writers Association as the coordinator of social media and the organization's internship program, as well as the poetry editor for CWA's *The Write City Magazine*. To learn more about Christina, visit her at **crodonline.info** or @poemlust on Instagram.

- Claire Thom is a Scottish poet, writer, and teacher who currently lives in the south of Spain. She is the founder and editor of *The Wee Sparrow Poetry Press*. Claire has had poetry published in several independent presses and five of her poems were long-listed for the Erbacce Poetry Prize in 2021. Find her on Instagram @poetrycadiz and @theweesparrowpoetrypress.

- Courtney Written is an artist and aspiring poetry writer from the Midwest who hopes to continue to share her words and connect with the world through this unique medium.

- Daniel J. Flore III's poems have appeared in many publications. His fifth poetry book is *Written in the Dust on the Ceiling Fan*, published by *Dead Man's Press Ink*.

- Daniel Moreschi is a poet from Neath, South Wales, UK. After life was turned upside down by his ongoing battle with severe M.E., he rediscovered his passion for poetry that had been dormant since his teenage years. Writing has served as a distraction from his struggles ever since. Daniel has been acclaimed by numerous poetry competitions, including *The Oliver Goldsmith Literature Festival, the Westmoreland Arts & Heritage Festival, The Utah State Poetry Society's Annual Spring Contest, the Jurica-Suchy Nature Museum's Nature Poetry Contest,* and the *Hugo Dock Snow Maze Poetry Contest*. Daniel has also had poetry published by *The Society of Classical Poets* and *The Black Cat Poetry Press*.

- Eddie Brophy is a poet, author, and blogger from Massachusetts. His poetry has appeared in several literary publications including *Better Than Starbucks, Ghost City Press,* and *Terror House Magazine*. His award-winning debut novel *Nothing to Get Nostalgic About*, is available now on Amazon and wherever you get your books. His first poetry collection *Autumn's Eulogy*, from *BookLeaf Publishing* is available on Amazon now. You can read his blog at eddiebrophywriter.weebly.com and follow him on Instagram @eddiebrophywriter

- Effie Spence, a multi-hyphenate storyteller and Aegean Sea witch, has the goal in life to be ridiculous, to make the mundane into magic, and to sometimes let herself dance to a song she likes playing in the grocery store. Effie works full time as an actor in Los Angeles and is producing original experimental films among other pursuits. She recently coined her personal philosophy; optimistic nihilism, meaning if nothing matters, we might as well choose what matters to us and she chooses joyful play. In her writing, she hopes to inspire that joie de vivre.

- Emily Eerie is a queer Latina poet living in the American south. Her work focuses on issues pertaining to trauma, gender, sexuality, and identity. More of her work can be found at @eerie_poetry on Instagram.

- Emily Perina (aka ESP) is a New York based artist. Her crafts range from mixed media sculpture, to poetry, to welding, and most recently, taxidermy. Her passion is to consistently strive to find just the perfect medium to convey complicated feelings. She often centers her work around attempting to accept her anxieties while pushing herself to adapt new practices to portray these feelings in her work. Found objects and items from nature are featured heavily and mirror her need to discard emotions into the artwork she creates.

- Emily Perkovich is EIC of Querencia Press, as well as an Art Evaluator for Persephone's Daughters from the Chicago-land area. Her work strives to erase the stigma surrounding trauma victims and their responses. Her piece *This is*

Performance-Art was a finalist for the 50th New Millennium Writings Award and she is a 2021 Best of the Net nominee. She is previously published with Cathexis Northwest, Coffin Bell Journal, and Awakened Voices among others. She is the author of the poetry collection Godshots Wanted: Apply Within and the novella Swallow. You can find more of her work on IG @undermeyou

- Emma Wells is a mother and English teacher. She has poetry published with and by *The World's Greatest Anthology, The League of Poets, The Lake, The Beckindale Poetry Journal, Dreich Magazine, Drunken Pen Writing, Porridge Magazine, Visual Verse, Littoral Magazine, The Pangolin Review, Derailleur Press, Giving Room Magazine, Chronogram* and for the *Ledbury Poetry Festival.* She also has published a number of short stories and her first novel, *Shelley's Sisterhood*, is due to be published shortly.

- Estelle Grace Tudor is a multi-genre award-winning author from the beautiful South Wales coast in the UK, where she lives with her husband, four children and crazy dog. She has independently published a five-book middle grade fantasy series and has been published in numerous magazines and anthologies. Her debut book placed in the top ten *of The Book Bloggers' Novel of the Year Awards*, and also won a Bronze Award in *The Wishing Shelf Book Awards.* She is currently working on an adult fantasy series, which she hopes to start publishing later this year.

- Faye Alexandra Rose is a poet and copywriter and the author of three poetry chapbooks: *Incognito (Bottlecap Press), Mortal Beings (Dark Thirty Poetry Publishing)*, and *Pneuma (Sunday Mornings at the River)* which was shortlisted for a *Saboteur Award* for Best Poetry Pamphlet. She graduated with first-class honours in Creative and Professional Writing and English Literature and is currently studying for an MA in Creative Writing.

- Fiona Dignan is a stay-at-home mum of four young children, based in London, UK. She started writing poetry and short fiction during lockdown to cope with the mayhem of homeschool. Her work is mostly based around themes of feminism, motherhood, nature, identity, sexuality and language.

- Gabrielle Pelayo is an emerging author from Hoffman Estates, IL. Her short stories, flash fiction, and poetry have been featured in a handful of publications and websites, including *Binge Magazine, Solstice Literary Magazine*, and with the *Heartland Society of Women Writers.* She is currently enrolled as an undergraduate student at Columbia College Chicago, where she is pursuing a creative writing major and a voiceover minor.

- Georgina Melendez is a Mexican-American poet born in good old Laredo, Texas. She moved to New York City with her mom at the age of 13 after her parents divorced. She fell in love with the concrete jungle and instantly became a city girl. After graduating high school, she attended a Vocational Institute where she became a Certified Medical Assistant and worked in Oncology for 15 years. These were some of the most challenging and best years of her life. She currently resides in Dallas, Texas with her wonderful husband. She works from home and also serves her spiritual community. She is an abstract poet at best, and she loves to take the reader into a maze full of heart tugs. She is deeply grateful for the written word and her connection to it.

❖ Ishita Ganguly is a published author, poet, and freelance writer from India. She is the author of the book, *"Stories from the City called Kolkata"*. Her articles and poems have been published on leading websites and in international magazines. Ishita is a double master's degree holder, a corporate professional turned educator turned full-time writer. She is a book lover who believes words have immense power and writers can make a huge impact in the world. You can contact her at www.ishitaganguly.com and on Instagram @iamauthorishita

❖ Jessica Berry grew up in the seaside town of Bangor, County Down. She is an English teacher at the Belfast Model School for Girls - the best reason possible for her to get out of bed each morning! In 2021, Jessica was placed in Bangor's annual poetry contest hosted by the Aspects Literary Festival. Her work has also been included in publications such as *Drawn to the Light* and *A New Ulster*.

❖ Jillian Calahan (she/her/they) is a poet and short story writer from Seattle, Washington. When she's not writing you can find her in a bookstore, chilling with her 4 cats and 2 dogs, crafting, or taking too many pictures of pretty sunsets. You can find her work on Instagram @novamarie_poetry

❖ Joe Espinoza is 46 years old and previously unpublished. He was born in Mexico, and his parents came to the U.S. in the late 70s. Some of his early memories are of them working in strawberry fields to give him and his brothers a good life. He now lives in southern California where he enjoys classic poetry and writing with a modern aesthetic.

❖ Jordan Nishkian is an Armenian-Portuguese writer based in California. Her prose and poetry explore themes of duality and have been featured in national and international publications. She is the Editor-in-Chief of *Mythos* literary magazine and author of *Kindred*, a novella.

❖ Kait Quinn was born with salt in her wounds. She flushes the sting of living by writing poetry. Her work has appeared or is forthcoming in *Reed Magazine*, *Crosswinds Poetry, Chestnut Review, VERSES*, and others. By day, Kait is a legal assistant living in Minneapolis with her partner, their regal cat (Spart), and their very polite Aussie mix (Jesse).

❖ Kate MacAlister is an author, feminist activist and bio-medical scientist. Her works have been published in journals and anthologies all over the world. Her poems are stories of human connection and the dreams of revolution. Coffee, her cat Bella, and her feminist friends are particularly important for her creative process. Find Kate on Instagram @kissed.by_fire

- Kristiana Reed (she/her) is a writer and the editor of *Free Verse Revolution*. She lives in the UK and has been publishing her work online since 2016. She has two poetry collections available for purchase - *Between the Trees* and *Flowers on the Wall*.

- Lev Verlaine is a trans poet from Washington State.

- Lilith Kerr is a queer Canadian poet, artist, and activist. Taking inspiration from writers such as Richard Siken, Natalie Wee, and Shani Mootoo, they explore themes of sapphic love and feminism. In addition, she is incredibly passionate about human rights advocacy, with a focus on LGBTQ+ rights, anti-capitalism, and decolonization. They also take a strong interest in philosophy, art, environmental sustainability, and languages. When Lilith isn't writing overly-angsty queer poetry, she can be found tutoring, painting, or making tiny sculptures of cats. You can find more of their work on Instagram @lilithkerr_art.

- Lindsay Valentin is a queer writer and letterpress artist living and working in Los Angeles. She has written for magazines and publications such as *BUST, GO NYC, Odyssa*, and *Pink Pangea*. Her poetry focuses on the darker workings of the creative mind and life, and making known those pieces of culture, including LGBTQ culture and experience, that may be lesser known.

- Elizabeth Yew (She/They) writes under the nickname "Liz Yew" and has had poems published physically and digitally since she began focusing on writing poetry. Liz grew up in Hong Kong and is now working through a BA in English literature and creative writing in the UK. She never understood poetry growing up, but since discovering Sylvia Plath's work, their own collection of depressing and reflective poetry, along with occasionally cheerful ones, quickly grew. However, being away from home does mean missing her dogs, which they compensate for with her newfound hobby of crocheting.

- Madeleine S. Cargile is a current student at Chelsea High School set to graduate with honors in May of 2022. She plans to pursue a neuroscience major at Auburn University in the fall. Along with reading and writing, she enjoys art, heavy metal music, and embroidery.

- Marisa Silva-Dunbar's work has been published in *ArLiJo, Chanterelle's Notebook, Pink Plastic House, Sledgehammer Lit, Analogies & Allegories Literary Magazine*. She has work forthcoming in *The Bitchin' Kitsch*. Her second chapbook, "*When Goddesses Wake*," was released in December, 2021 from *Maverick Duck Press*. Her first full-length collection, "*Allison*," was recently published by *Querencia Press*. You can find her on Twitter and Instagram @thesweetmaris. To check out more of her work go to www.marisasilvadunbar.com

- Michael Brigden is a passionate writer best known under his penname 'The Ordinary Poet'. As The Ordinary Poet his poems can be found on Facebook, Twitter and Instagram. Michael is an incurable romantic who loves nothing better than to spend time with his wife and kids who are very often his inspiration. He is fascinated, awed and sometimes angered by the world around him, this is reflected within his body of work.

- Mimi Flood has published her first collection of poetry called Nosebleed on Amazon. She has been published in *The Underground Literary Journal, Electric Cereal, Dark Thirty Poetry Publishing, The Graveyard zine*, and *Gypsophila*. You can find her on Instagram @Marigold_Jesus

- Nabila Abid is from Jaipur, India. She is in her final year of graduation pursuing Political Science Honours. An avid reader and a good listener. In her pastime, she can be found reading and writing poetry which will have a social issue attached to it as well as taking care of her plants. She believes more in words and silences than humans.

- Omobola's education started at the University of Lagos Staff School, then Federal Government Girls College, Sagamu in Ogun State, Nigeria's southwestern region, Africa. She has a B.Sc and M.Sc in Microbiology from the University of Lagos. Currently, she works as an account representative in Chicago, where she lives with her family.

- PD Hogan is a musician and writer from the foothills outside of Yosemite. He has a BA in english and philosophy from Fresno State. When he isn't writing stories, he's writing music for one of his metal bands and spoiling his cat, Logan Hogan.

- Pop is a university student from France, currently at Sheffield Hallam University on the Erasmus programme. She aspires to be a writer, and mostly writes poetry for the time being, but stories have always been a huge part of her life, and she dreams of bringing some more into the world. You can follow her at @sunflowers_adventure on Instagram where she posts short pieces or snippets of her projects.

- Rachel Jacobs, also known by her penname, Phantasma, holds two Bachelors of Art degrees from California State University Long Beach in Creative Writing and Literature. She explores themes such as the non-conscious theme of emotions, nature, and self-identity/the human experience. Her poetry publications are found in *Humana Obscura, Harness Magazine*, and on *Vocal*. Phantasma continues to make an impression in the writing world, and she thanks you greatly for reading.

- Rebecca Green is a poet and illustrator based in West Yorkshire, UK. Her writing is rooted in honesty and truth, with particular focus on race, motherhood and mental health. Rebecca was mentored by Kim Moore for the 2021 Ilkley Literature Festival and was selected as a New Northern Poet. Other works can be found @rebeccagreenpoetry on Instagram.

- Rhys grew up in Cardiff, Wales - the place that molded him to be the person he is today. However in 2018 he returned to his birthplace where he now resides. Since moving back he has honed his poetry skills and developed his love for the art form further. IG @rhysc.ampbell

- Robin Williams (she/they) is a queer poet and practicing witch from Pennsylvania. They've had previous publications in the *Horizon Literary Magazine, Moss Puppy magazine, Warning Lines magazine, Free Verse Revolution magazine*, and many more. Her full poetry collection, In the Mid-Hours, is out now with *Raine and Rose Co.* Instagram: @by.robinw Website: www.greenferncoven.com

- ❖ Ryan is a poet from the West Midlands in the UK. He started writing poetry as a way to express and understand his thoughts and emotions in order to escape the clutches of depression. Through writing, Ryan has found a way to explore and share his emotions, which has earned him the moniker of the 'King of Romance' amongst some fellow writers. You can find Ryan's work in his two self-published books, *20/20 Vision* and *Heart in the Clouds*, both available on Amazon, or by finding him on social media - Instagram: @r5k.poetry Facebook: R5K Poetry Twitter: @R5KPoetry Tiktok: @r5kpoetry

- ❖ Sana Mujtaba is a housewife, and mother of three beautiful kids from Pakistan. She has been writing poetry since the age of 13 and always been sensitive to the happenings around her. That led her to pick up her pen. She joined the IG community in 2019. Initially, it was fun to write for pages and prompts but now she only writes when she feels inspired. Her poetry is published in several international anthologies. Instagram @sana.m.writes

- ❖ Sara Sabharwal is a poetess, author, traveler, wife, and mother. Her ambition is to leave the world more beautiful than she found it. Drawing inspiration from her own life, she uses words to paint vivid pictures dripping in imagery. You can find her on Instagram @words.wrapped.in.lace

- ❖ Sarah Corwin is a visual artist and recent poet living in Seattle, WA. Her poems have been featured in *Pile Press* and *Delicate Emissions*, and are forthcoming in *Bullshit Lit*. You can get in touch with her on Instagram @dontlookpoems.

- ❖ Sascha Felix Luinenburg (@Deepfakedichter) is a young poet living and working in the Netherlands. His work seeks to explore and celebrate the experience of trying to situate oneself in a world that is simultaneously too human and not human enough. Both the author and his work are confused, happy, and afraid. They long for weightlessness.

- ❖ Savannah Verdin, Nonfiction EIC of *Querencia Press*, is a New Orleans native working as a domestic violence community outreach advocate with Pillars Community Health in Chicago and a peer mentor with NAMI. She partners with community agencies to educate, empower, and guide communities in a collaborative effort to eradicate domestic violence. As a trauma survivor she has lived experience to create comfort for other survivors as they find safety from violence, rebuild their lives, and recover their voice. You can find her on IG @influentialpencil

- ❖ Shilo Niziolek's cnf manuscript, Fever, was first runner-up in *Red Hen Press's* Quill Prose Prize and a finalist in *Zone 3 Press's* 2021 CNF Award. Her work has appeared in *[PANK], Juked, Entropy, HerStry*, among others, and is forthcoming in *the CLR, Gingerbread House* and *Pork Belly Press's* zine: *Love Me, Love My Belly*. Shilo holds an MFA from New England College and is Associate Faculty at Clackamas Community College.

- Stephanie Parent is a lifelong lover of fairy tales and an author of poetry and prose. Born and raised in Baltimore, Maryland, she now considers Los Angeles her true home. Stephanie's poetry has been nominated for a Rhysling Award and Best of the Net.

- T.C. Anderson is a Houston-based writer and artist with work published in *Venus Rising: Musings & Lore from Women Writers*, *Pages Penned in Pandemic: A Collective*, *Capsule Stories*, and more. Her short story, "Letter to the Boy at the Grocery Store," was the winner of *Poetic Reveries*'s Christmas Short Story Competition in 2021. Her poetry chapbook, *The Forest*, serves as the basis of an art installation with artist Mari Omori premiering in 2022. Her artistic work has been shown in Houston, online, and internationally. Anderson holds a B.A. in Graphic Design & Media Arts from Southern New Hampshire University.

- Tiggy Chadwick is a young woman from Reading, UK. Her work primarily lies in portraiture, however, she also writes poetry in much a similar way to portray a person on canvas. Her writing aims to make the reader feel as though they are looking into the eyes of another and understanding them.

- Tom Squitieri is a three-time winner of the Overseas Press Club and White House Correspondents' Association award for work as a war correspondent. Tom is blessed to have his poetry appear in more than 35 publications, anthologies, art shows, and the film "Fate's Shadow: The Whole Story," where he shared the Los Angeles Motion Picture Festival "Grand Jury Prize Gold for Monologues & Poetry." He writes most of his poetry while parallel parking or walking his dogs, Topsie and Batman

- Tyler Hurula (she/her) is a poet born and raised in Denver, Colorado. She is queer, polyamorous, and a pet parent to two cats. Her poems have been published previously in *Anti-Heroin Chic and Aurum Journal*, *Rat's Ass Review, and Gnashing Teeth Publishing*. Her poems feature love, polyamory, family, growing up, and being queer. She values are connection, authenticity, and vulnerability, and tries to encompass these values in her writing as well as everyday life.